D1135089

Lovers, Mates, and Strange Bedfellows

Other books by James R. Foster

THE WORLD'S GREAT FOLKTALES

GREAT FOLKTALES OF WIT AND HUMOR

LOVERS, MATES, AND STRANGE BEDFELLOWS

OLD-WORLD FOLKTALES

Arranged and Edited by James R. Foster

HARPER & BROTHERS   NEW YORK

For
Susan Ann French

Contents

Preface

These particular old-world folktales were selected because they were the most interesting and readable ones found among the many which tell curious stories about lovers, mates, and queer bedfellows. There was a real need to bring these little masterpieces of folk narrative art out of the old books and journals where they lay virtually forgotten, and to spread them forth upon mint-new printed pages for all who read to enjoy. After all, they are a precious part of our literary heritage.

The reader will discover that these tales always tell a good story. They are full of ancient lore, odd primitive beliefs and superstitions, and the elemental stuff of human life. Their world is a magic one of marvels and romance; a world with a "logic" which delights the imagination.

The best versions available have been followed, no liberties being taken with the substance of the narratives. But for the sake of clarity obsolete words and old idiomatic expressions have been replaced by modern ones. Some superfluous introductions and clearly extraneous or tediously repetitious passages have been either cut out or condensed. A very few tales have been shortened, this being always indicated in the notes.

If a good English translation of a tale in a foreign language could not be found, it has been translated, the endeavor being made to remain faithful to the text and spirit of the original. The notes at the end of the book supply information about each individual tale.

J. R. F.

Lovers, Mates, and Strange Bedfellows

1. The Scar

ONCE UPON a time there was a king. This king had an only
son, and one day the son went out to hunt. After walking a
long time, God knows how long, he saw an old man whose
hair bristled like a lion's mane, seated at the side of the road,
and he was writing in a book.

"Old father, what are you writing?" asked the prince.

"Never mind, royal prince. You came here to hunt, so be on
your way." When the prince insisted on knowing, the old
man said, "I write down the sins and the fates of men—that
is, their destiny."

"Well, old father, tell me mine."

"Why not, prince?" said the venerable man. "I will tell
you, but you may repent your curiosity. There is a cowherd
in a certain village, and this man has a daughter whose body
is swollen and covered with ulcers. She is leprous, and there
is no way to cure her. That girl will one day be your wife!"

After having heard this, the prince returned home full of
bitterness and gloom. "Son, why are you so pale and downcast?" asked the king and queen. Then the prince told them
what the old man had said. "You can't escape your fate," said

they. "God's mercy be praised. What He has written on a man's brow, He has written."

A few days after this the prince filled his wallet with gold coins, mounted a horse and set out for the village where the cowherd lived. He found the house and knocked at the door. The cowherd's wife opened. "Mother," said the king's son, "could you lodge a stranger?" "Why not, prince royal? It is God who sends the guest. But this is only a cowherd's house and hardly fit to entertain a prince in."

"The house suffices," said the prince. "I am not going to stay a year. If you will lodge me tonight, tomorrow I will depart."

The woman was pleased that the prince deigned to stop in her house. She ushered him in, set him down on a mattress and placed food before him. When in the evening the cowherd came home, he was abashed, seeing a prince there. Why would such a great man wish to lodge in such a humble house? "A thousand welcomes, royal prince," said the poor herd. "How are you? May your visit be blessed!"

During supper the prince asked the cowherd, "If it is not indiscreet to inquire, how many children have you?" "Two sons and two daughters" was the answer. Just then deep sighs came from the next room. "What are those sighs?" asked the guest. "If I conceal it from you, how can I hide it from God?" said the herd. "I have a sick daughter. For seven years her belly is swollen, and she is covered with ulcers. The poor girl is neither living nor dead. We are all waiting for God to take her soul and deliver her from her suffering. And we are almost as much to pity as she is, for of what good is her life?" The prince bit his tongue and said to himself, "Yes, that's certainly the girl the old man meant."

Soon after supper he went to bed. Late in the night he arose, took the wallet full of gold coins and quietly entered the room where the sick girl lay. He gripped a great poniard in his fist, and suddenly he plunged it into the girl's abdomen. Instantly her groans ceased and she lay still. Thinking that he had killed her, the prince said to himself, "Now, how can she be my destined bride?" Thrusting the bloody poniard and the wallet full of gold (as blood money) under the girl's pillow, he mounted his horse and returned home.

Now his poniard had not touched the girl's intestines, but the opening it made reduced the swelling and stopped the pain. On awakening, the cowherd and his wife found that their guest had left, and, more surprising still, they did not hear their daughter's usual moaning. They rejoiced for they thought that she was dead and that now they could summon the priest to carry her to church.

But what a surprise when they saw her! The swelling had all disappeared and she was in a deep, deep sleep. Lifting her pillow, they found the bloody poniard and the wallet full of money. Neither poniard nor their daughter now held their attention. They could think of nothing but those gold coins, and the sight of them filled their hearts with sudden joy and great bliss. The girl slept for a day—for two days, and for three! And then she slowly came awake. How amazing! she was entirely well and perfectly sound. No sign of her ever having been sick remained on her after a month or two. And she became so beautiful that her equal could not have been found in the whole world. She was a perfect nymph! Whenever a man saw her, he lost his mind and said to himself, "I do not wish to eat or drink or even dress—all I desire is to feast my eyes on this charming figure, this lithe form as beautiful as a poplar swaying in the breeze."

By means of the prince's gold the cowherd became a wealthy man. He had houses built, each with a pretty veranda. The villagers were surprised and asked themselves, "How could this poor cowherd, who hardly had enough to eat, do all this?"

One day the prince, who was on a hunting trip, found himself quite by chance in this village. As he was walking along one of the streets, he looked up and saw a gracious and marvelously beautiful maiden on a veranda. Instantly he fell so deeply in love with her that he feared he would lose his reason.

With head bent low and with a feeling of deep depression he returned home. His father, seeing him so sad, asked him, "O my son, why are you so haggard and woebegone? If some secret in your heart tortures you, tell me what it is! Do you love the daughter of some merchant? Of some king? Tell me where she dwells and I will ask for her immediately." The prince told him about the girl on the veranda. "It is she and no other," said he, "that I wish to marry. No other maiden, whether daughter of merchant or king, exists as far as I am concerned. That one has fallen like a drop of blood into my heart."

"Why, my son," asked the king, "are you so cast down over a simple matter like this? Still, there may be obstacles and impediments you have not mentioned. Speak. If she can be had, tell me, and without delay I will send a messenger to ask her father for her."

"O send him, my father; that is all I wish."

The king sent the messenger. How could the girl's father say "no"? Where could he find a better son-in-law? So he said, "I will gladly give the prince permission to marry my daughter and am greatly honored, indeed."

So the cowherd's daughter and the king's son were betrothed and soon afterwards married. For seven days and nights after the wedding there was feasting and dancing and all kinds of merrymaking. Then one day the newly married couple went to the baths. When she had taken off her clothes, a scar about an inch from her navel caught his attention. "Dear wife," he asked, "what is that scar?" Then she told him all that had happened to her. When he heard this, he bit his finger to the bone. "Blessed be thy dispensations, O God," thought he. "The old man said the truth when he told me that this woman would become my wife!"

And now he told her his story. Struck by the wonder of it, the husband and wife looked fixedly at each other for a long time. What God has written on a man's brow, He has written, and no man can escape his fate.

◆◆◆◆◆

2. The Goat-Girl

THERE WAS ONCE a husbandman with his wife who had no children. His wife besought God to give her a child though it were no better than a kid. In course of time she accordingly gave birth to a kid. It grew up and became a fine she-goat. Her mother said to her once on a time, "Who will take water for your father to the field?" Said she, "Fasten it to my horn and

I will take it." So she fastened it and she took it to her father. On her return she found a sunny spot where she took off her hide to clean it.

As a prince passed by to go to the chase, he saw her, and his eyes were dazzled with her beauty, which shone like the sun. When she saw the prince, she straightway went into her hide and set off home. The prince sent people to follow her and watch where she went in. Then he returned to his mother and said, "Send to say I am suitor for the hand of the she-goat."

When his mother heard that, she began to wail and beat her breast, and said, "My son, if you want to marry, take a princess."

"Nay," said he, "but I will take her."

His mother saw his distress and affliction and sent two women to get the goat. The mother of the she-goat took a cudgel to them. "Why have you come to mock me?" said she, "a woman who has no daughter—only this goat that God has given me to console me!"

So the women went back and told the treatment they had met with.

The prince said to his mother, "Go yourself."

So, willy-nilly, she went and said to the she-goat's mother, "There is no help for it!"

The latter was so frightened when she saw the queen that she let her have the goat. So the queen took her and brought her to her son. Then her son was glad, for he had eaten no bread for five days for grief.

One day the queen made ready to knead a cake; the she-goat came with her horn and tore the dough to bits. So the queen hit her a whack with the rolling pin. The next day the

maid took the bread and put it into the oven. The she-goat
went frisking by her side, and when she reached the oven the
goat went and spoiled the loaf with her horn. The cook seized
the shovel and hit her a bang with it.

At that time the cousin of the king was to be married, and
her father invited her kinsfolk to the wedding. So they made
ready and went to the wedding, and tied the goat to a bench.
When they were all gone and the goat left by herself, she laid
aside her hide and dressed herself in golden embroidery and
went to the wedding also. She sat by her future mother-in-
law, who, when she saw her beauty, said to herself, "Would
that such a one were my son's wife!" So she asked her,
"Whence do you come, my child?"

"From the rolling pin," said she.

She went down to dance and danced. When her betrothed
saw her he knew her, and when the dance slackened she flung
down a golden apple and put on her hide and fled. In the
evening the queen came home with her son and said, "Did
you see a fair woman at the dance?"

Said her son, "I did. But did not you ask her whence she
came?"

And she said, "Yes, but I don't know what she said. I did
not hear aright."

"If she comes tomorrow, mind you ask her again, mother!"
said her son. On the morrow they all went again to the marriage festivities. And the goat-girl also went, and she sat by
the queen. So she asked her, "Whence come you, my child?"
Said she, "From the fire shovel."

Then she went down to dance and danced. When the dance
slackened, again she flung down a golden apple so as to astonish
the people that she might get away. Again she put on her

hide and sat down, tied by the bench. The prince did not know how to get the hide off her.

In the evening he came home again with his mother and asked, "Mother, did you ask where that fair one came from?"

"She told me, my son, but I have forgotten."

In the morning the prince arose and went to the cook and said to him, "Make the oven very hot and don't bake bread for anyone, because you give me no cake." Then he said to his mother, "Go you to the marriage feast—I will come later on."

So they all went out, and he shut himself up in a neighboring house. The goat-girl put off her hide and went to the feast. The prince seized the skin and flung it in the oven. The smell of the singeing hide came to her nostrils, and she left the dance and rushed to cast herself into the oven. The prince burst forth and seized her—and said to her, "I don't mean you for the oven, my lady!" And he took her in his arms and shut her in the glass chamber. And he went no more to the feast but stayed with her. His mother sent the nurse to see why her son did not come, and the nurse said to him, "Why did you not come to the feast?"

"I have a headache," he said. "Let my mother enjoy herself and I will come in later on."

So the queen waited, but he did not come. So she set off and went home alone. Then the prince said to her, "See, mother, take the key and bring me a mug from the glass chamber."

As she went to open the door, the chamber shone. She uttered a loud cry and told him there was a fairy in the chamber. And the prince laughed and said, "You have good eyes, mother!"

Then he took her by the hand and they went in together. And the bride came and kissed her hand. The prince said, "See, mother, that's the goat!"

Then the queen embraced her and said to her, "My child, why have you not shown yourself all this long time?"

And straightway on the morrow the queen went and called all her royal kinsfolk to the wedding. And she invited the mother and father of the bride as well. But they were afraid lest they should behead them. And they told the king they were afraid and would not come. Then the king had clothes made for them and went himself and brought them. And their daughter came to meet them and kissed her hand to them from the foot of the staircase and welcomed them. The wedding was celebrated and the prince and his bride lived happily.

⚜⚜

3. King O'Hara's Daughters

THERE WAS a king in Desmond whose name was Coluath O'Hara, and he had three daughters. On a time when the king was away from home, the eldest daughter took a thought that she'd like to be married. So she went up in the castle, put on the cloak of darkness which her father had, and wished for the most handsome man under the sun as a husband for herself.

She got her wish; for scarcely had she put off the cloak of

darkness when there came in a golden coach with four horses, two black and two white, the finest man she had ever laid eyes on, and took her away.

When the second daughter saw what had happened to her sister, she put on the cloak of darkness and wished for the next best man in the world as a husband. She put off the cloak, and straightway there came in a golden coach with four black horses a man nearly as good as the first, and took her away.

The third sister put on the cloak and wished for the best white dog in the world. Presently he came, with one man attending, in a golden coach and four snow-white horses, and took the youngest sister away.

When the king came home, the stableboy told him what had happened while he was gone. He was enraged beyond measure when he heard that his youngest daughter had wished for a white dog and gone off with him.

When the first man brought his wife home, he asked, "In what form will you have me in the daytime—as I am now in the daytime, or as I am now at night?"

"As you are now in the daytime."

So the first sister had her husband as a man in the daytime; but at night he was a seal.

The second man put the same question to the middle sister and got the same answer. So the second sister had her husband a man by day and a seal by night.

When the third sister came to where the white dog lived, he asked her, "How will you have me to be in the daytime—as I am now in the day, or as I am now at night?"

"As you are now in the day."

So the white dog was a dog in the daytime but the most handsome of men at night.

After a time the third sister had a son; and one day when her husband was going out to hunt, he warned her that if anything should happen to the child, not to shed a tear on that account.

While he was gone, a great gray crow that used to haunt the place came and carried the child away when it was a week old. Remembering the warning, the mother shed not a tear for the loss. All went on as before till another son was born. The husband used to go hunting every day, and again he said she must not shed a tear if anything happened. When the child was a week old a great gray crow came and bore him away, but the mother did not cry or drop a tear.

All went well till a daughter was born. When she was a week old a great gray crow came and swept her away. This time the mother dropped one tear on a handkerchief, which she took out of her pocket and then put back again. When the husband came home from hunting and heard what the crow had done, he asked the wife, "Have you shed tears this time?"

"I have dropped one tear," said she.

Then he was very angry, for he knew what harm she had done by dropping that one tear.

Soon after, their father invited the three sisters to visit him and be present at a great feast in their honor. They sent messages, each from her own place, that they would come. The king was very glad at the prospect of seeing his children; but the queen was grieved and thought it a great disgrace that her youngest daughter had no one to come home with her but a white dog.

The white dog was in dread that the king wouldn't leave him inside with the company but would drive him out of the castle into the yard, and that the dogs outside wouldn't leave a patch of skin on his back but would tear the life out of him. His wife comforted him. "There is no danger for you," said she, "for wherever I am you'll be, and wherever you go I'll follow and take care of you."

When all was ready for the feast at the castle, and the company was assembled, the king was for banishing the white dog; but the youngest daughter would not listen to her father— would not let the white dog out of her sight but kept him near her at the feast and divided with him the food that came to herself. When the feast was over and all the guests had gone, the three sisters went to their own rooms in the castle.

An hour or so later the queen took the cook with her and stole in to see what was in her daughters' rooms. They were all asleep at the time.

What should she see by the side of her youngest daughter but the handsomest man she had ever laid eyes on. Then she went to where the other two daughters were sleeping; and there, instead of the two men who brought them to the feast, were two seals, fast asleep! At the sight of the seals the queen was greatly troubled. When she and the cook were returning, they came upon the skin of the white dog. She caught it up as she went and threw it into the kitchen fire. The skin was not five minutes in the fire when it gave a crack that woke not only all in the castle but all in the country for miles around.

The husband of the youngest daughter sprang up. He was very angry and very sorry and said, "If I had been able to spend three nights with you under your father's roof, I should have got back my own form again for good and could have been a man both in the day and night. But now I must depart."

He rose from the bed, ran out of the castle, and away he

went as fast his two legs could carry him, overtaking the one
before him and leaving the one behind. He ran all that night
and the next day. But he couldn't leave his wife, for she followed from the castle, was after him in the night and the day
too, and never lost sight of him.

In the afternoon he turned and told her to go back to her
father, but she would not listen to him. At nightfall they came
to the first house they had seen since leaving the castle. He
turned and said, "Do you go inside and stay in this house till
morning; I'll pass the night outside where I am." The wife
went in. The woman of the house rose up, gave her a pleasant
welcome and put a good supper before her. She was not long
in the house when a little boy came to her knee and called her
"mother." The woman of the house told the child to go back
to his place and not to come out again.

"Here are a pair of scissors," said the woman of the house
to the king's daughter, "and they will serve you well. Whatever ragged people you see, if you cut a piece off their rags,
that moment they will have new clothes of cloth of gold." She
stayed that night, for she had good welcome. Next morning
when she went out, her husband said, "You'd better go home
now to your father." "I'll not go to my father if I have to
leave you," said she.

So he went on and she followed. It was that way all the day
till night came; and at nightfall they saw another house at the
foot of a hill, and again the husband stopped and said, "You
go in; I'll stop outside till morning." The woman of the house
gave her a good welcome. After she had eaten and drunk, a
little boy came out of another room, ran to her knee and said,
"Mother." The woman of the house sent the boy back to
where he had come from and told him to stay there.

Next morning when the princess was going out to her husband, the woman of the house gave her a comb and said, "If you meet any person with a diseased and a sore head and draw this comb over it three times, the head will be well and covered with the most beautiful golden hair ever seen." She took the comb and went out to her husband. "Leave me now," said he, "and go back to your father."

"I will not," said she, "but I will follow you while I have the power." So they went forward that day as on the other two. At nightfall they came to a third house, at the foot of a hill, where the princess received a good welcome. After she had eaten supper, a little girl with only one eye came to her knee and said, "Mother." The princess began to cry at the sight of the child, thinking that she herself was the cause that it had but one eye. Then she put her hand into her pocket where she kept the handkerchief on which she had dropped the tear when the gray crow carried her infant away. She had never used the handkerchief since that day, for there was an eye on it. She opened the handkerchief and put the eye in the girl's head. It grew into the socket that minute, and the child saw out of it as well as out of the other eye; and then the woman of the house sent the little one to bed.

Next morning as the king's daughter was going out the woman of the house gave her a whistle and said, "Whenever you put this whistle to your mouth and blow on it, all the birds of the air will come to you from every quarter under the sun. Be careful of the whistle, as it may serve you greatly."

"Go back to your father's castle," said the husband when she came to him, "for I must leave you today." They went on together a few hundred yards and then sat on a green hillock, and he told the wife, "Your mother has come between us.

But for her we might have lived together all our days. If I had been allowed to pass three nights with you in your father's house, I should have got back my form of a man both in the daytime and the night. The Queen of Tir-nan-Og (the land of youth) enchanted and put on me a spell, that, unless I could spend three nights with a wife under her father's roof in Erin, I should bear the form of a white dog one half of my time; but, if the skin of the dog should be burned before the three nights were over, I must go down to her kingdom and marry the queen herself. And 'tis to her I am going today. I have no power to stay, and I must leave you. So farewell, you'll never see me again on the upper earth."

He left her sitting on the mound, went a few steps forward to some bulrushes, pulled up one and disappeared in the opening where the rush had been.

She stopped there, sitting on the mound lamenting till evening, not knowing what to do. At last she bethought herself, and, going to the rushes, pulled up a stalk, went down, followed her husband and never stopped till she came to the lower land. After a while she reached a small house near a splendid castle. She went into the house and asked could she stay there till morning. "You can," said the woman of the house, "and welcome."

Next day the woman of the house was washing clothes, for that was how she made a living. The princess fell to and helped her with the work. In the course of that day the Queen of Tir-nan-Og and the husband of the princess were married.

Near the castle and not far from the washerwoman's lived a henwife with two ragged little daughters. One of them came around the washerwoman's house to play. The child looked so poor and her clothes were so worn and dirty that the princess took pity on her and cut the clothes with the scissors which she had. That moment the most beautiful dress of cloth of gold ever seen on woman or child in that kingdom was on the henwife's daughter. When she saw what she had on, the child ran home to her mother as fast as ever she could go. "Who gave you that dress?" asked the henwife. "A strange woman that is in that house beyond," said the little girl, pointing to the washerwoman's house.

The henwife went straight to the Queen of Tir-nan-Og and said, "There is a strange woman in the place who will be likely to take your husband from you unless you banish her away or do something to her, for she has a pair of scissors different from anything ever seen or heard of in this country." When the queen heard this she sent word to the princess that unless the scissors were given up to her without delay, she would have the head off her.

The princess said she would give up the scissors if the queen would let her pass one night with her husband. The queen answered that she was willing to give her the one night. The princess came and gave up the scissors and went to her own husband. But the queen had given him a sleeping draught, and he fell asleep and never woke till after the princess had gone in the morning.

Next day another daughter of the henwife went to the washerwoman's to play. She was wretched-looking, her head being covered with scabs and sores. The princess drew the comb three times over the child's head, cured it, and covered it with beautiful golden hair. The little girl ran home and told her mother how the strange woman had drawn the comb over her head, cured it, and given her beautiful golden hair. The henwife hurried off to the queen and said, "That strange woman has a comb with wonderful power to cure and give golden hair; and she'll take your husband from you unless you banish her or take her life."

The queen sent word to the princess that unless she gave up the comb she would have her life. The princess returned as answer that she would give up the comb if she might pass one night with the queen's husband. The queen was willing and gave her husband a drugged drink as before. When the princess came, he was fast asleep and did not waken till after she had gone in the morning.

On the third day the washerwoman and the princess went out to walk, and the first daughter of the henwife with them. When they were outside the town, the princess put the whistle to her mouth and blew. That moment the birds of the air flew to her from every direction in flocks. Among them was a bird of song and new tales. The princess went to one side with the bird. "What means can I take," asked she, "against the queen to get back my husband? Is it best to kill her, and can I do it?"

"It is very hard," said the bird, "to kill her. There is no one in all Tir-nan-Og who is able to take her life but her own husband. Inside a holly tree in front of the castle is a ram, in the ram a duck, in the duck an egg, and in that egg is her heart and life. No man in Tir-nan-Og can cut that holly tree but her husband." The princess blew the whistle again. A fox and a hawk came to her. She caught and put them into two boxes which the washerwoman had with her, and took them to her new home.

When the henwife's daughter went home, she told her mother about the whistle. Away ran the henwife to the queen and said, "That strange woman has a whistle that brings together all the birds of the air, and she'll have your husband yet unless you take her head." "I'll take the whistle from her, anyhow," said the queen. So she sent for the whistle.

The princess gave answer that she would give up the whistle if she might pass one night with the queen's husband. The queen agreed and gave him a draught as on the other nights. He was asleep when the princess came and when she went away.

Before going, the princess left a letter with his servant for the queen's husband. In this she told how she had followed him to Tir-nan-Og and had given the scissors, the comb and the whistle to pass three nights in his company, but had not spoken to him because the queen had given him sleeping draughts; that the life of the queen was in an egg, the egg in a duck, the duck in a ram, the ram in a holly tree in front of the castle, and that no man could split the tree but himself.

As soon as he got the letter the husband took an ax and went to the holly tree. He found the princess there, and she had the two boxes with the fox and the hawk in them.

He struck the tree a few blows; it split open, and out sprang the ram. He ran scarce twenty rods before the fox caught him. The fox tore him open; then the duck flew out. The duck had not flown fifteen rods when the hawk caught and killed her, smashing the egg. That instant the Queen of Tir-nan-Og died.

The husband kissed and embraced his faithful wife. He gave a great feast; and when the feast was over he burned the hen-wife with her house, built a palace for the washerwoman, and made his servant secretary.

They never left Tir-nan-Og and are living there happily now; and so may we live here.

❧❧❧

4. Absent Without Leave

THERE WAS BEFORE a regiment in Dublin in Erin, and it was going a long journey. There was a sergeant, a corporal, and a private, who had sweethearts in the town. They went to see them on the day that they were to go, and they stayed too long, and the regiment left them. They followed it, and they were going and going till the night came on them.

They saw a light a long way from them; and if it was a long way from them, it was not long they were in reaching it. They went in; the floor was ready swept, and a fire on it, and no one in. They sat at the fire toasting themselves. They were not long there when the private rose, to whom was the name of John, to look what was in the chamber, because there was a light in it. There was there a board covered with every sort of meat, and a lighted candle on it. He went up; he began to eat, and the others began to hinder him, for that he had no business with it. When they saw that he did not stop, they went up and they began themselves.

There were three beds in the chamber, and one of them went to lie in each bed. They had not laid long when three great red girls came in, and one of them stretched herself near each one of the soldiers. And when the girls saw the time fitting in the morning, they rose, ate breakfast, and went away. And there was a splendid breakfast on the board for the soldiers too.

The sergeant said that they had better follow the regiment, but John said that they should not; that as long as he could get food and rest he would not go. When dinnertime came they sat and they took their dinner. The sergeant said they had better leave, but John did not agree. When suppertime came they sat and ate; afterwards they went to lie down, each one to his own bed. The girls came this night too and went to lie down as before. In the morning they rose and went away.

This day was like the one before it, the three soldiers doing full justice to the feasts which regularly appeared on the magic board, the sergeant saying they should depart and John arguing that to do so would be foolish. When it was night they went to lie down. The girls came and they lay down near them.

In the morning the eldest girl gave the sergeant a purse, and every time he would unloose it, it would be full of gold and silver. "What will thou give to thine?" she asked the middle one. "I will give him a tablecloth and every time he spreads it, it will be full of every sort of food." She gave it to the corporal; and she said to the youngest, "What wilt thou give to thine own?" "I will give him a whistle, and every time he plays it he will be in the very middle of the regiment." She gave him the whistle; they left their blessing with the soldiers and went away.

"I won't let it rest here," said John. "I will know who they are before I go further forward." He followed them, and he saw them going down a glen; and when he was about to be down, they came to meet him, and they were weeping. "What is the matter with you?" says he.

"Much is the matter with us," said they, "that we are under charms till we find three lads who will spend three nights with us without putting a question to us; and if thou hadst stayed without following us we were free."

"Is there any way that you can get free but that?" said he.

"There is," said they. "There is a tree at the end of a certain house" (and they told him where he could find it), "and if you come at the end of a day and year and pluck up the tree, we were free."

John turned back where the rest were, and he told them how it happened to him and that he had promised the girls to pluck up the tree. Now they gave this advice to each other that they should return back to Dublin again because it was not worth their while to follow the regiment. They returned back to Dublin.

That night John said, "I think I will go see the king's daughter tonight." "Thou hadst better stay in the house," said the others, "than go there."

"I will go there, at all events," says he. He went and he reached the king's house and struck at the door. One of the gentlewomen asked him what he wanted, and he said he wished to be speaking to the king's daughter. The king's daughter came where he was, and she asked what business he had with her. "I will give thee a whistle," said he, "and when thou playest it, thou wilt be in the middle of such a regiment." When she got the whistle, she drove him downstairs and shut the door on him.

"How went it with thee?" asked the other soldiers. "She wheedled the whistle from me," said John. He did not stop till he had beguiled a loan of the purse from the sergeant. "I had better," said John, "go to see the king's daughter again." He went away and he reached the house; he saw the king's daughter. She wheedled the purse from him and drove him downstairs, as she did before; and he turned back. He did not stop till he beguiled a loan of the tablecloth from the corporal. He went again where the king's daughter was. "What wilt thou give me this journey?" she asked. "A tablecloth, and when it is opened it will be full of every sort of eatables." "Let me see it," said she. "We will spread it out," said he. He spread it out, and there was a corner that would not lie right. He said to her to stand on the corner; she stood on it. He stood himself on another corner. Then he wished to be in the uttermost isle of the deep; and himself and the king's daughter and the tablecloth were in it in five minutes!

There was the very prettiest island that man ever saw, and nothing in it but trees and fruits. There they were, going through the island backwards and forwards, and sleep came on him. They came to a pretty little hollow, and he laid his head in her lap; and he took a death grip on her apron in order that she should not get away without his perceiving her.

When he slept she loosed the apron; she left him there; she took the tablecloth and standing on it wished herself to be in her father's house. And she was in it.

When John awoke he had nothing to get; he had nothing to see but trees and birds. He was then keeping himself alive with the fruits of the island, and hit upon apples. And when he would eat one sort of them they would put a deer's head on him. When he would eat another sort of them they would put it off him. One day he gathered a great many of the apples of both kinds. He saw a vessel going past and waved to her. A boat came to shore, and they took him on board.

The ship carried him to Dublin. As soon as he was ashore, he made straight for the king's palace. He cried, "Apples for sale! Apples for sale!" and saw the king's daughter put her head out of the window. She asked that a pound of apples should be sent up to her. He said she should try how they would agree with her first. He threw up an apple to her of the sort that would put a deer's head and horns on her. The king sent forth word that if any man whatsoever could be found who would heal his daughter, that he should get a peck of gold, and a peck of silver, and herself to marry.

She was thus many days and no man coming that could do any good at all. In his ragged clothes John came to the door, asking to get in, but, when they saw his like, they would not let him enter. But the princess had a little brother, and he saw them keeping John out and he told his father. The king said, "Let him in though he be a beggar of the green!" So John was admitted, and they took him up to the chamber where the princess was. She did not recognize him. He sat and he took a book out of his pocket, with nothing in it, pretending that he was reading it. "Didst thou," said he, "wheedle a whistle from a poor soldier; when he would play it, it would take him to the middle of the regiment?" "I wheedled," said she. "If that is not found," said he, "I cannot heal thee." "It is," says she. They brought the whistle to him. Then he gave her a piece of apple, and one of the horns fell off her. "I can't," said he, "do more today, but I will come here tomorrow."

Then he went out, and his old comrades met him. The trade they had was to be slaking lime and drawing water for stone masons. He knew them, but they did not know him. He noticed nothing at all, but he gave them ten shillings and said, "Drink the health of the man who gave them."

On the morrow he went where the king's daughter was. He took out the book and said to her, "Didst thou wheedle a purse from a poor soldier, that would be full of gold and silver every time it was opened?" "I wheedled," said she. "If that is not found," said he, "I cannot heal thee." "It is," said she; and they gave him the purse. Then he gave her a piece of the apple and another horn fell off her. "I can do no more today," said he, "but I will come the next night."

He went where his old comrades were, and he gave them another ten shillings and said, "Drink the health of the man who gave them."

He returned the next night to see the king's daughter. He gave a pull at the book as he used to do. "Didst thou wheedle," said he, "a tablecloth from a poor soldier that would be full of every kind of food every time it was undone?" "I wheedled," said she. "If that cloth is not to be found, I cannot cure thee," says he. "It is," says she. They gave it to him. As quick as he got it, he gave her a whole apple; and when she ate it she was as she was before. Here he got a peck of gold and a peck of silver; and they told him he would get herself to marry. "I will come tomorrow," said he.

He went the way of his old comrades this time too. He gave them ten shillings and said, "Drink the health of the man who gave them." Said they, "It would be pleasing to us to know what kind friend is giving us the like of this every night." "Do you remember," said John, "the three great red girls and the promise to pull up a tree a year from the time?" Then they knew him! "That time has gone past long ago," said they. "It is not gone," said he. "Next night is the night."

On the morrow he went past the king's palace, and the king's daughter said to him, "Art thou going to marry me today?" "No, nor tomorrow," said he. He returned to where the rest were, and he began to set them in order for going to the magic tree. He gave the purse to the sergeant, the tablecloth to the corporal, and the whistle he kept himself. He bought three horses, and they went riding with great haste. When they reached the house they took hold of the tree, and it came out of the ground at the first pull. The three red girls came so white and smiling where they were, and they were free from the spells. Every man of them took his own with him. They came back to Dublin, and they married.

❦❦❦

5. The Wind Rider

A MAGICIAN WAS once upon a time much put out with a young countryman, and being in a great rage he went to the man's hut and stuck a new sharp knife under the threshold. While he did so, he cursed the man, saying, "May this fellow ride for seven years on the fleet storm wind until he has gone all round the world."

Now when the peasant went into the meadows in order to rake up the hay, there came suddenly a gust of wind. It quickly scattered the hay and then seized the peasant. He tried in vain to resist; in vain he sought to cling to the hedges and trees with his hands. Do what he would, the invisible power hurried him forwards.

He flew on the wings of the wind like a wild pigeon, and his feet no more touched the ground. At length the sun set, and the poor fellow looked with hungry eyes upon the smoke which curled up from the chimneys in his village. He could almost touch them with his feet, but he called and screamed in vain, and all his wailing and complaints were useless. No one heard his lamentation; no one saw his tears.

And this continued for three months, and what with thirst and hunger he was dried up and almost a skeleton. By that time he had gone over a good deal of ground, but the wind most often carried him over his native village. He wept when he saw the hut in which dwelt his sweetheart. He could see her busied about the house. Sometimes she would bring out some dinner in a basket. Then he would stretch out his dried-up hands to her and vainly call her name. His voice would die away, and the girl, not hearing him, would not look up.

He fled on. The magician came to the door of his hut, and, seeing the man, cried to him mockingly, "You have to ride for seven years yet, flying over this village. You shall go on suffering and shall not die."

"O my father," cried the man, "if I ever offended you, forgive me! Look! my lips are quite hard; my face, my hands— look at them! I am nothing but bone. Have pity upon me."

The magician muttered a few words, and the man stopped in his course. He stayed in one place, but did not yet stand on the ground.

"Well, you ask me to pity you," said the magician. "And what do you mean to give me if I put a stop to your torment?"

"All you wish," said the peasant, and he clasped his hands and assumed a kneeling position in the air.

"Will you give me your sweetheart," asked the magician, "so that I may have her for my wife? If you will give her up, you shall come to earth again."

The man in the air thought a moment and said to himself, "If I once get on the earth again, I may see if I cannot do something." So he said to the magician, "Indeed, you ask me to make a great sacrifice, but if it must be so, it must."

The magician then blew at him, and the man came to the ground. He was very much pleased to find the earth once more under his feet and to have escaped from the power of the wind. Off he hurried to his hut, and at the threshold he met his sweetheart. She cried aloud with amazement when she saw the long-lost peasant she had so long lamented and wept for. With his skinny hands the man put her gently aside and went into the house, where he found the farmer who had employed him, sitting down. Commencing to weep, the poor fellow said to him, "I can no longer stay in your service, and I cannot marry your daughter. I love her very much, as much as the apple of my eye, but I cannot marry her."

The old farmer wondered to see him, and when he saw his white pinched face and the traces of his suffering, he asked him why he did not wish for the hand of his daughter. The man told him all about his ride in the air and the bargain he had made with the magician. When the farmer had listened to it all, he told the poor fellow to keep a good heart, and putting some money in his pocket, he went out to consult a sorceress.

Towards evening he returned very merry, and, taking the peasant aside, said to him, "Tomorrow morning, before day-break, go to the witch and you will find all will be well."

The wearied peasant, who had not slept for three months, went to bed, but he awoke before it was day and went off to the witch. He found her sitting beside the hearth boiling herbs over a fire. She told him to stand by her, and suddenly, although it was a calm day, such a storm of wind arose that the hut shook again.

The sorceress then took the peasant outside into the yard and told him to look up. He lifted up his eyes and—O wonder! —saw the evil magician whirling round and round in the air.

"There is your enemy," said the woman. "He will trouble you no more. If you would like to see him at your wedding, I will tell you what to do, but he must suffer the torment that he meant to put you to."

The peasant was delighted and ran back to the house. A month later he was married. While the wedding folk were dancing, he went out into the yard, looked up and saw right over the hut the magician turning round and round. Then the peasant took a new knife, and, throwing it with all his strength, stuck it in the magician's foot.

The evil man fell at once to the ground, and the knife pinned him to the earth so that he could only stand at the window and see how merry the peasant and his friends were.

The next day he had disappeared, but he was afterwards seen flying in the air over a lake. Before him and behind him were flocks of ravens and crows, and these, with their hoarse cries, heralded the wicked magician's endless ride on the wind.

ᥱᢹᢒᢌᥱᢹᢒᢌ

6. *The Perspiring Lover*

PERHAPS MERE HEARSAY is not often capable of creating love, yet it has happened. Prince Nala, ruler of Nichada, had never seen Damayanti, the daughter of King Bhima, but he had often heard her virtues and beauty praised. According to popular report Indra himself was so taken with her charms that he yearned to make her his wife. To listen to those who sang the perfections of this maiden filled the prince's heart with rapture. Likewise, listening to talk about the accomplished and handsome Prince Nala gave Damayanti a strange and delicious pleasure. It is thus that Kama, the god of love, slyly enters into unsuspecting hearts.

One day Nala went into the forest. He pretended to hunt but actually spent most of the time dreaming about Damayanti. Some migratory swans chancing to alight near him, he seized one of them. He was greatly surprised when it spoke to him.

"O Prince," it said, "if you spare my life and let me go, I will speak such words to Damayanti that she will never love anyone but you."

So he let the swan go. The snow-white bird flew directly to Damayanti, who was frolicking with some ladies in the garden of her father's palace, and it whispered in her ear, "Charming princess, Nala, the handsomest of men, is the only mate worthy of you, the most beautiful of women."

The swan flew away. The princess stood motionless, as if stunned. The message had gone straight to her heart. Instantly uncertainty vanished: she loved this prince. She loved him very much. Soon she became languid. There was a drawn look about her. She began to lose her fresh color. Play delighted her no more and she slept badly at night. Her women, worried and baffled, ran to her father and described her condition. He knew immediately what the matter was—she was fifteen and it was time to marry her off. After consulting his ministers, he had the bells rung and proclaimed his daughter's *swayam-bara,* that is, the concourse of suitors, one of whom she would publicly choose for her husband.

At this announcement there was a great stir in heaven and earth. All the gods and kings aspiring to wed Damayanti set out for King Bhima's capital city. Among the first was Prince Nala. His chariot was drawn by magnificent elephants wreathed in flowers. Four of the gods saw him passing and marveled at the beauty of this mortal. Descending to earth, they addressed him. "Nichada," they said, "you have always shown us due reverence. And today we have need of your services. Will you be our agent in an affair of great importance?"

"I will do whatever you request," he replied.

"Look at us," they said, "if your eyes can bear the radiance of our glory. Before you stand Indra, Agni, Varuna and Yama. We are all suitors for the hand of the fair Damayanti. Go to her, announce our coming and make her see the advantages of choosing a god for her husband."

"Immortal gods," cried Nala, "do you ask this of me? How can I plead your cause when I go to plead my own? Tell me, would a woman listen to a lover arguing the advantages of marrying one of his rivals? Moreover, the mere sight of the fair one who has captured my heart will strike me dumb."

"You have promised," said the gods in chorus, "and you cannot go back on a promise. Now, no more talk from you. Obey!"

By their magic power the gods sent Nala through the air and set him down beside Damayanti's bed. She had just fallen asleep. Nala gazed on her exquisite beauty; she was a jewel beyond compare. In the presence of such flawless perfection he trembled.

When the women of the seraglio perceived that a man was in their midst, they screamed with alarm. However, as soon as they lit the lamps and saw how handsome the intruder was, their fear quickly changed to admiration. The noise awoke Damayanti. Opening her great dark eyes, she saw Nala for the first time. "Say quickly who you are," cried she. "You must have come on the wings of a genie, for how else could you have entered here?"

"I am Nala, noble princess," said he. "The gods sent me here by magic. Indra, Agni, Varuna, and Yama forced me to be their ambassador. They are suitors for your hand and have sent me to persuade you to choose one of them for your husband."

Damayanti smiled sweetly. She saw that Nala was having difficulty getting out his message and supposed that his task was distasteful to him.

"I revere the gods," said she, "but I have chosen you to be my husband. Have you not guessed? Love for you consumes me, and it was in hope of becoming your wife that I had the assembly of kings convoked."

This tender declaration did not make it any easier for Nala to speak in behalf of the gods. However, he made an effort to make the princess understand the advantages of wedding a divinity. But it was of no use. "I love you, Nala," she said. "In my eyes you are infinitely more desirable than any one of the gods. If you will not have me, I will seek the remedy of my love pangs in either poison, fire or water."

"If the gods suspect that I have played them false, do you not fear, my well-beloved, that those powerful beings will take vengeance upon me?"

"Have not the gods learned that a woman will have her way? They cannot blame you for a choice she has made. To-morrow at my *swayambara* I shall choose you for my husband.

How could the gods find fault with a woman's selecting a mate her heart had already spoken for? However, if the divinities are resentful, their anger will fall on me as the only one responsible. And now adieu, noble warrior, leave us before you are discovered."

Nothing was spared to make the *swayambara* a magnificent affair. In the center of a gigantic amphitheater a platform supported by gold pillars had been erected for the suitors to stand on. It was a great sight to see the kings and gods there with their long curled hair, their arched eyebrows, their shining eyes, their earrings sparkling with precious stones. They were like great lions on a mountain.

The appearance of the princess was greeted with a great cry of admiration. Two hundred women, her usual retinue, followed her. All carried silk parasols and bright-colored banners. The suitors, each in his turn, passed slowly before the princess. However, when it was Nala's turn, the four gods joined him, at the same time assuming his form and appearance. How was Damayanti to know which was Nala?

"O gods," she cried, "do you think this tricky procedure fair play? Hear my prayer. Conceal no longer your divine characteristics."

Because her soul was pure, they could not refuse her petition. When she looked again at her five suitors, she noticed that four of them floated in the air, their toes an inch or so from the floor. These four did not blink their eyes or perspire or become sullied by dust or dirt. And their bodies cast no shadows. Turning her attention to the fifth suitor, she saw that his feet touched the floor, that his shadow stretched across the platform, and that he blinked his eyes. Furthermore, sweat ran down his forehead and his garlands had begun to wilt.

This was Nala! So she threw her wreath around his neck. Thus the choice of the royal virgin was declared.

All who were there applauded—all but the gods. They did not try to hide their bad humor. It was a great blow to their pride that Damayanti should pass them by to give her preference to a mere mortal. Although Bhima secretly regretted not getting a god for a son-in-law, he did not oppose the marriage and the wedding was an extraordinarily splendid one.

7. *Strange Liaison*

ON THE BANKS of the river Danh in Annam there dwelt a pretty maiden and her widowed mother. They lived quite alone. One night, about the time of the third watch, two strangers came to their door, knocked and asked to be admitted. Supposing these to be some of their kith or kin, the women rose from their bed, threw on some clothing, lit the lamp and opened the door. In stepped a young man of about twenty, and after him came his servant. The young man was very handsome, but his servant had a most hideous face. Terribly frightened, the women fled to a back room.

"Dear women," said the young man, "we will do you no harm. We intend nothing but kindness. Please come forth and listen to what I have to say."

"Go and hide in the garden, daughter," whispered the widow. "As I am old and my life of little worth, I will take the risk of a parley with our visitors." Thereupon she came into the room where the men were.

"Madam," said the young man, "your daughter is very beautiful, and she has captured my heart. Whatever you wish shall be yours if you will permit me to be her lover. Here, take this precious jewel as a pledge. It shines so brightly it will light all the house; you will not need your lamp."

"If you take my daughter away," said the widow, "I would be left in the house all alone. I would not like that." Then, as she supposed this princely youth could be nothing but an otherworld being, she added, "Besides, it is hardly possible that the ways of your world are those of ours."

"Do not let these matters afflict you," said the stranger. "If you agree to my proposal, your daughter shall remain here in this house with you, and I will come to visit her here. Only once a month will I come. And I will supply money, provisions—anything you can name. However, if you reject my proposal, I tell you plainly, I will have the maiden anyway."

At that moment day began to spring in the east. Hastily the two men reached under the bed where they had hidden their serpent skins and slipped quickly into them. Then they left the house and plunged headlong into the river.

The mother and daughter were frightened out of their wits. Summoning their kinsfolk, they explained what had happened and asked for advice. Some said one thing, some another, but no one could hit upon a remedy for the plight of the widow and her daughter. Most were of the opinion that it would be best to agree to the proposal of the river god or sprite, for such they deemed him to be.

Not until a month had passed did the would-be lover appear. Indeed, the two women had begun to hope that he would never come. But one night in the second watch they heard a great splashing in the river. Three figures emerged from the water. Each bore a huge salver heaped high with precious stones, silver and gold. These were the wedding presents. The bearers of the salvers came into the house, put them down and returned to the river.

It was not long before their master appeared. From that night on, once each month he came to visit his paramour. And this continued for five or six years. However, at last, for some reason or another, the affair ended. "Someday you will surely have another lover," said the river sprite by way of a farewell, "and when this happens you have my permission to marry him, if you wish."

If the maid had anything to say to this quitclaim, doubtless meant to be extremely generous, it has not been recorded.

❧❧❧❧

8. Sea Wife

ON THE SHORE of Smerwick harbor one fine summer's morning, just at daybreak, stood Dick Fitzgerald "shoghing the dudeen," which may be translated, smoking his pipe. The sun was gradually rising behind the lofty Brandon, the dark sea was getting green in the light and the mists clearing away out of the valleys went rolling and curling like the smoke from the corner of Dick's mouth.

" 'Tis just the pattern of a pretty morning," said Dick,

taking the pipe from between his lips and looking towards the distant ocean, which lay as still and tranquil as a tomb of polished marble. "Well, to be sure," continued he after a pause, " 'tis mighty lonesome to be talking to one's sclf by way of company and not to have another soul to answer one—nothing but the child of one's own voice, the echo! I know this: that if I had the luck, or maybe the misfortune," said Dick, with a melancholy smile, "to have a woman, it would not be this way with me! And what in the wide world is a man without a wife? He's no more, surely, than a bottle without a drop of drink in it, or dancing without music, or the left leg of a scissors, or a fishing line without a hook, or any other matter that is noways complete. Is it not so?" said Dick Fitzgerald, casting his eyes towards a rock upon the strand, which, though it could not speak, stood up as firm and looked as bold as ever Kerry witness did.

But what was his astonishment at beholding, just at the foot of that rock, a beautiful young creature combing her hair, which was of a sea-green color; and now the salt water shining on it appeared in the morning light like melted butter upon cabbage.

Dick guessed at once that she was a merrow, although he had never seen one before, for he spied the *cohuleen driuth*, or little enchanted cap which the sea people use for diving down into the ocean, lying upon the strand near her. And he had heard that, if once he could possess himself of the cap, she would lose the power of going away into the water; so he seized it with all speed, and she, hearing the noise, turned her head about as natural as any Christian.

When the merrow saw that her little diving cap was gone, the salt tears—doubly salt, no doubt, from her—came trickling down her cheeks, and she began a low mournful cry, with just the tender voice of a newborn infant. Dick, although he knew well enough what she was crying for, determined to keep the *cohuleen driuth*, let her cry never so much, to see what luck would come of it. Yet he could not help pitying her; and when the dumb thing looked up in his face, and her cheeks all moist with tears, 'twas enough to make anyone feel, let alone Dick, who had ever and always, like most of his countrymen, a tender heart of his own.

"Don't cry, my darling," said Dick Fitzgerald; but the merrow, like any bold child, only cried the more for that.

Dick sat himself down by her side and took hold of her hand by way of comforting her. 'Twas in no particular an ugly hand, only there was a small web between the fingers, as there is in a duck's foot; but 'twas as thin and as white as the skin between egg and shell.

"What's your name, my darling?" says Dick, thinking to make her conversant with him. But he got no answer, and he was certain sure now either that she could not speak or did not understand him. He therefore squeezed her hand in his as the only way he had of talking to her. It's the universal language, and there's not a woman in the world, be she fish or lady, that does not understand it.

The merrow did not seem much displeased at this mode of conversation; and, making an end of her whining all at once, "Man," says she, looking up in Dick Fitzgerald's face, "man, will you eat me?"

"By all the red petticoats and check aprons between Dingle and Tralee," cried Dick, jumping up in amazement. "I'd as soon eat myself, my jewel! Is it I eat you, my pet? Now, 'twas some ugly ill-looking thief of a fish put that notion into your own pretty head, with the nice green hair down upon it, that is so cleanly combed out this morning!"

"Man," said the merrow, "what will you do with me if you won't eat me?"

Dick's thoughts were running on a wife. He saw at the first glimpse that she was handsome, but, since she spoke, and spoke too like any real woman, he was fairly in love with her. 'Twas the neat way she called him "Man" that settled the matter entirely.

"Fish," says Dick, trying to speak to her after her own short fashion. "Fish," says he, "here's my word, fresh and fasting, for you this blessed morning, that I'll make you Mistress Fitzgerald before all the world, and that's what I'll do."

"Never say the word twice," says she. "I'm ready and willing to be yours, Mr. Fitzgerald. But stop, if you please, till I twist up my hair." It was some time before she had settled it entirely to her liking; for she guessed, I suppose, that she was going among strangers, where she would be looked at. When that was done, the merrow put her comb in her pocket and then bent down her head and whispered some word to the water that was close to the foot of the rock.

Dick saw the murmur of the words upon the top of the sea going out towards the wide ocean, just like a breath of wind rippling along, and, says he, in the greatest wonder, "Is it speaking you are, my darling, to the salt water?"

"It's nothing else," said she, quite carelessly. "I'm just sending word home to my father not to be waiting breakfast for me, just to keep him from being uneasy in his mind."

"And who's your father, my duck?" said Dick.

"What!" said the merrow. "Did you never hear of my father? He's the king of the waves to be sure."

"And yourself, then, is a real king's daughter?" said Dick, opening his two eyes to take a full and true survey of his wife that was to be. "Oh, I'm nothing else but a made man with you, and a king your father. To be sure he has all the money that's down at the bottom of the sea!"

"Money," repeated the merrow. "What's money?"

" 'Tis no bad thing to have when one wants it," replied Dick; "and maybe now the fishes have the understanding to bring up whatever you bid them?"

"Oh, yes," said the merrow, "they bring me what I want."

"To speak the truth, then," said Dick, " 'tis a straw bed I have at home before you, and that I'm thinking is noways fitting for a king's daughter. So if 'twould not be displeasing to you just to mention a nice feather bed, with a pair of new blankets—but what am I talking about? Maybe you have not such things as beds down under the water?"

"By all means," said she. "Mr. Fitzgerald—plenty of beds at your service. I've fourteen oyster beds of my own, not to mention one just planting for the rearing of young ones."

"You have?" says Dick, scratching his head and looking a little puzzled. " 'Tis a feather bed I was speaking of; but clearly yours is the very cut of a decent plan to have bed and supper so handy to each other that a person, when they'd have the one, need never ask for the other."

However, bed or no bed, money or no money, Dick Fitzgerald determined to marry the merrow, and the merrow had given her consent. Away they went therefore across the strand, from Gollerus to Ballinrunnig, where Father Fitzgibbon happened to be that morning.

"There are two words to this bargain, Dick Fitzgerald," said his reverence, looking mighty glum. "And is it a fishy woman you'd marry? The Lord preserve us! Send the scaly creature home to her own people; that's my advice to you, wherever she came from."

Dick had the *cohuleen driuth* in his hand and was about to give it back to the merrow, who looked covetously at it; but he thought for a moment, and then says he, "Please your reverence, she's a king's daughter."

"If she was the daughter of fifty kings," said Father Fitzgibbon, "I tell you, you can't marry her, she being a fish."

"Please your reverence," said Dick again, in an undertone, "she is as mild and as beautiful as the moon."

"If she was as mild and as beautiful as the sun, moon and stars, all put together, I tell you, Dick Fitzgerald," said the priest, stamping his right foot, "you can't marry her, she being a fish!"

"But she has all the gold that's down in the sea only for the asking, and I'm a made man if I marry her; and," said Dick, looking up slyly, "I can make it worth anyone's while to do the job."

"Oh, that alters the case entirely," replied the priest. "Why, there's some reason now in what you say. Why didn't you tell me this before? Marry her by all means, if she was ten times a fish. Money, you know, is not to be refused in these bad times, and I may as well have the handsel of it as another that maybe would not take half the pains in counseling you that I have done."

So Father Fitzgibbon married Dick Fitzgerald to the merrow, and, like any loving couple, they returned to Gollerus well pleased with each other. Everything prospered with Dick; he was at the sunny side of the world. The merrow made the best of wives, and they lived together in the greatest contentment.

It was wonderful to see, considering where she had been brought up, how she would busy herself about the house, and how well she nursed the children; for at the end of three years there were as many young Fitzgeralds—two boys and a girl.

In short, Dick was a happy man, and so he might have continued to the end of his days if he had only had the sense to take proper care of what he had got. Many another man, however, beside Dick, has not had wit enough to do that.

One day, when Dick was obliged to go to Tralee, he left the wife minding the children at home after him, and thinking she had plenty to do without disturbing his fishing tackle. Dick was no sooner gone than Mrs. Fitzgerald set about cleaning up the house, and, chancing to pull down a fishing net, what should she find behind it in a hole in the wall but her own *cohuleen driuth*. She took it out and looked at it, and then she thought of her father the king, and her mother the queen, and her brothers and sisters, and she felt a longing to go back to them.

She sat down on a little stool and thought over the happy days she had spent under the sea. Then she looked at her children and thought on the love and affection of poor Dick, and how it would break his heart to lose her. "But," says she, "he won't lose me entirely, for I'll come back to him again, and who can blame me for going to see my father and my mother after being so long away from them?"

She got up and went towards the door but came back again to look once more at the child that was sleeping in the cradle. She kissed it gently, and as she kissed it a tear trembled for an instant in her eye and then fell on its rosy cheek. She wiped away the tear, and, turning to the eldest little girl, told her to take good care of her brothers, and to be a good child herself until she came back. The merrow then went down to the strand. The sea was lying calm and smooth, just heaving and glittering in the sun; and she thought she heard a faint, sweet singing, inviting her to come down. All her old ideas and feelings came flooding over her mind. Dick and her children were at the instant forgotten, and placing the *cohuleen driuth* on her head she plunged in.

Dick came home in the evening, and missing his wife he asked Kathelin, his little girl, what had become of her mother, but she could not tell him. He then inquired of the neighbors, and he learned that she was seen going towards the strand with a strange-looking thing like a cocked hat in her hand. He returned to his cabin to search for the *cohuleen driuth*. It was gone, and the truth now flashed upon him.

Year after year did Dick Fitzgerald wait, expecting the return of his wife, but he never saw her more. Dick never married again, always thinking that the merrow would sooner or later return to him, and nothing could ever persuade him but that her father the king kept her below by main force. "For," said Dick, "she surely would not of herself give up her husband and her children."

While she was with him she was so good a wife in every respect that to this day she is spoken of in the tradition of the country as the pattern for one, under the name of The Lady of Gollerus.

⊷⧫⊷⧫⊷

9. The Swan Princess

THERE WAS ONCE a king in Erin, and he had an only son. While this son was a little child his mother died. After a time the king married and had a second son. The two boys grew up together; and as the elder was far handsomer and better than the younger, the queen became jealous and was for banishing him out of her sight.

The king's castle stood near the shore of Lough Erne, and three swans came every day to be in the water and swim in the lake. The elder brother used to go fishing; and once, when he sat at the side of the water, the three swans made young women of themselves, came to where he sat and talked to him.

The queen had a boy minding cows in the place, and when he went home that night he told about what he had seen— that there were three young women at the lake and the king's son was talking to them that day. Next morning the queen called the cowherd to her and said, "Here is a pin of slumber; and do you stick it in the clothes of the king's son before the young women come. And when they go away, take out the pin and bring it back to me."

That day when the cowherd saw the three young women coming, he went near and threw the pin, which stuck in the clothes of the king's son. That instant he fell asleep on the ground. When the young women came, one of them took a towel, dipped it in the cold water of the lake and rubbed his face; but she could not rouse him. When their time came to go, they were crying and lamenting because the young man was asleep. And one of the three put a gold pin in his bosom so that when he woke up he would find it and keep her in mind. After they had been gone a couple of hours, the cowherd came up, took out the sleeping pin and hurried off. The king's son woke up without delay; and finding the gold pin in his bosom, he knew the young women had come to see him.

Next day he fished and waited again. When the cowherd saw the young women coming out of the lake, he stole up a second time and threw the pin, which stuck in the prince's clothes, and that moment he was drowsy and fell asleep. When the maidens came he was lying on the ground asleep. One of them rubbed him with a towel dipped in the water of the lake; but no matter what she did, he slept on, and when they had to go, she put a gold ring in his bosom. When the sisters were leaving the lake and had put on their swan skins and become swans, they all flew around him and flapped their wings in his face to know could they rouse him; but there was no use in trying.

After they had gone, the cowherd came and took out the sleeping pin. When the king's son was awake he put his hand in his bosom, found the keepsake and knew that the sisters had come to him.

When he went fishing the third day, he called the cowherd and said, "I fall asleep every day. I know something is done to me. Now do you tell me all. In time I'll reward you well. I know my stepmother sends something by you that takes my senses away."

"I would tell," said the cowherd, "but I'm in dread my mistress might kill or banish me."

"She will not, for I'll put you in the way she'll not harm you. You see my fishing bag here? Now throw the pin, which I know you have, towards me and hit the bag." The cowherd did as he was told and threw the pin into the fishing bag where it remained without harm to anyone. The cowherd went back to his cattle, and the prince fished on as before.

The three swans were out in the middle of the lake swimming around for themselves in the water, and the prince moved on, fishing, till he came to a bend in the shore. On one side of him a tongue of land ran out into the lake. The swans came to the shore, leaving the piece of land between themselves and the prince. Then they took off their swan skins, were young women, and bathed in the lake. After that they came out, put on the dress of young women and went to where the king's son was fishing. He spoke to them and asked where were they from, in what place were they born and why were they swans.

They said, "We are three sisters, daughters of the King of the East, and we have two brothers. Our mother died, and our father married again and had two other daughters. These two are not so good-looking nor so well-favored as we, and their mother was in dread they wouldn't get such fine husbands as we, so she enchanted us, and now we are going about the world from lake to lake in the form of swans."

Then the eldest of the three sisters said to the king's son, "Who are your kinsmen and where were you born?"

"I was born in Erin," said he, "and when I was a little boy my mother died, my father married again and had a second son, and that son wasn't to the eye what I was, and my stepmother was for banishing me from my father's house because she thought her own son was not so good as I was, and I am fishing here every day by the lake to keep out of her sight."

"Well," said the eldest sister, "I knew you were a king's son, and so I came to you in my own form to know could we go on in the world together."

"I don't know yet what to do," said the prince.

"Well, be sure of your mind tomorrow, for that will be the last day for me here."

When the cowherd was going home, the king's son gave him the sleeping pin for the stepmother. When he had driven in the cattle, the cowherd told the queen that the young man had fallen asleep as on the two other days. But there was an old witch in the place who was wandering about the lake that day. She saw everything, went to the queen and told her how the three swans had made young women of themselves and talked with her stepson.

When the queen heard the old witch, she fell into a terrible rage at the cowherd for telling her a lie, and banished him out of her sight forever. Then she got another cowherd and sent him off with the sleeping pin next day. When he came near the lake, the king's son tried to drive him off; but the cowherd threw the sleeping pin into his clothes, and he fell down near the edge of the water without sight or sense.

The three sisters came and found him sleeping. They rubbed him and threw water in his face, but they could not wake him. And the three were lamenting sorely, for they had brought a swan's skin with them that day so the king's son might make a swan of himself and fly away with them, for this was their last day at that place. But they could do nothing now for he lay there dead asleep on the ground before them.

The eldest sister drew out her handkerchief, and the falling tears dropped on it. Then from the nipple of her left breast she snipped off a wee bit of flesh and wrapped it in the handkerchief. On the hem the second sister wrote, "Keep this memento until you hear from us again." They put it in his bosom and went away.

As soon as the sisters had gone, the cowherd came, pulled out the pin and hurried away. The stepmother was always trying to banish the king's son, hoping that something might happen to him, and her own son be the heir. So now he went off and wandered away through Erin, always inquiring for the eldest sister, but never could find her.

After returning home, he was fishing at the side of Lough Erne one day when a swan flew up to him and said, "Your love is lying on her deathbed, unless you go to save her. She is bleeding from the breast, and you must go to her now. Go straight to the East!"

The king's son went straight to the East, and on the way there rose up a storm and fog against him; but they did not stop him. He was going on always, and when he was three weeks' journey from his father's castle he stumbled one dark misty day and fell over a ditch. When he rose there stood on the other side of the ditch before him a little horse, all bridled and saddled, with a whip on the saddle. The horse spoke up and said, "If you are the king's son, I was sent here to meet you and carry you to the castle of the King of the East. There is a young woman at the castle who thinks it long till she sees you. Now ask me no questions, for I'm not at liberty to talk to you till I bring you to the East."

"I suppose we are to be a long time going?" said the king's son.

"Don't trouble yourself about the going; I'll take you safely. Sit on my back now and be sure you're a good rider, and you'll not be long on the road. This is my last word."

They went on and were going always; and as he traveled the prince met the wind that was before him, and the wind that blew behind could not come up with him. They went on sweeping over the world for many days, and when they were near their destination the horse said, "Get down from my back now, for it's tired I am. When you come to the castle, don't stop a moment till you ask where the young woman is lying."

When the prince came to the castle it was evening. The two younger sisters welcomed him. (These were two of the swans at the lake in Erin, and now at home by the enchantment of their stepmother. They were swans in the daytime and women only at night, so as not to be under the eye of young men when these came to see the stepmother's own daughters.) They said, "Our sister is on an island, and we'll go to her." They got a boat for the young man and went with him to where their sister was lying. They said to her, "The son of the King of Erin is here."

"Let him come in that I may look at him," said she.

The prince went in, and when she saw him she was glad. "Have you anything that belongs to me?" asked she.

"I have."

"Then throw it on my breast."

He threw the handkerchief on her breast and went away. Next day she rose from the bed as well as ever. On the third day after his arrival the son of the King of Erin married the eldest daughter of the King of the East, and the stepmother's enchantment was destroyed; and there was the grandest wedding that ever was seen in that kingdom.

A son and a daughter were born to them. Then the king's son made up his mind not to let his stepmother's son be heir to the kingdom in place of himself. So taking his wife and children, he left the East and traveled to Erin. He stopped on the road and sent word to the father that he was coming.

When the stepmother heard the news, a great weakness came on her. She fell into a fit and died.

The cowherd she had banished for telling about the sleeping pin was found and rewarded. When the king died, his eldest son became the ruler of Erin.

ك‍‍ﭬﺩ‍ﭬﺩ‍ك‍

10. Thomas Rymer

AS THOMAS OF ERCELDOUNE lay on Huntley bank, a place on the descent of the Eildon hills, which raise their triple crest above the celebrated monastery of Melrose, he saw a lady so extremely beautiful that he imagined it must be the Virgin Mary herself. Her appointments, however, were those rather of an Amazon or goddess of the woods. Her steed was of the highest beauty and spirit, and at his mane hung thirty silver bells and nine, which made music to the wind as she paced along. Her saddle was of ivory, laid over with goldsmith's work; her stirrups, her dress, all corresponded with her extreme beauty and the magnificence of her array. The fair huntress had her bow in her hand and her arrows at her belt. She led three greyhounds on a leash, and three ratches, or hounds of scent, followed her closely.

She rejected and disclaimed the homage which Thomas desired to pay to her; so that, passing from one extremity to the other, Thomas became as bold as he had at first been humble. The lady warns him that he must become her slave if he should prosecute his suit towards her in the manner he proposes. Before their interview terminates, the appearance of the beautiful lady is changed into that of the most hideous hag in existence; one side is blighted and wasted, as if by palsy; one eye drops from her head; her color, as clear as virgin silver, is now of a dun leaden hue. A witch from the spital or almshouse would have been a goddess in comparison to the late beautiful huntress.

Hideous as she was, Thomas's irregular desires had placed him under the control of this hag, and when she bade him take leave of the sun and of the leaf that grew on tree, he felt himself under the necessity of obeying her. A cavern received them, in which, following his frightful guide, he for three days traveled in darkness, sometimes hearing the booming of a distant ocean, sometimes walking through rivers of blood which crossed their subterranean path.

At length they emerged into daylight, in a most beautiful orchard. Thomas, almost fainting for want of food, stretches out his hand towards the goodly fruit which hangs around him, but is forbidden by his conductress, who informs him these are the fatal apples which were the cause of the fall of man. He perceives also that his guide had no sooner entered this mysterious ground and breathed its magic air than she revived in beauty, equipage and splendor, as fair as or fairer than he had first seen her on the mountain.

She then commands him to lay his head upon her knee and proceeds to explain to him the character of the country. "Yonder right-hand path," she says, "conveys the spirits of the blessed to paradise; yon downward and well-worn way leads sinful souls to the place of everlasting punishment. The third road, by yonder dark brake, conducts to the milder place of pain, from which prayer and mass may release offenders. But see you yet a fourth road, sweeping along the plain to yonder splendid castle? Yonder is the road to Elfland, to which we are now bound. The lord of the castle is king of the country, and I am his queen. But, Thomas, I would rather be drawn with wild horses than he should know what hath passed between you and me. Therefore, when we enter yonder castle observe strict silence and answer no question that is asked at you, and I will account for your silence by saying I took your speech when I brought you from middle earth."

Having thus instructed her lover, they journeyed on to the castle, and, entering by the kitchen, found themselves in the midst of such a festive scene as might become the mansion of a great feudal lord or prince. Thirty carcasses of deer were lying on the massive kitchen board, under the hands of numerous cooks, who toiled to cut them up and dress them, while the gigantic greyhounds which had taken the spoil lay lapping the blood and enjoying the sight of the slain game. They came next to the royal hall, where the king received his loving consort without censure or suspicion. Knights and ladies, dancing by threes (reels, perhaps), occupied the floor of the hall, and Thomas, the fatigues of his journey from the Eildon hills forgotten, went forward and joined in the revelry.

After a period, however, which seemed to him a very short one, the queen spoke with him apart and bade him prepare to return to his own country. "Now," said the queen, "how long think you that you have been here?" "Certes, fair lady," answered Thomas, "not above these seven days." "You are deceived," answered the queen. "You have been seven years in this castle; and it is full time you were gone. Know, Thomas, that the fiend of hell will come to this castle tomorrow to demand his tribute, and so handsome a man as you will attract his eye. For all the world would I not suffer you to be betrayed to such a fate; therefore up and let us be going." This terrible news reconciled Thomas to his departure from Elfin land, and the queen was not long in placing him upon Huntley bank, where the birds were singing. She took a tender leave of him, and to ensure his reputation bestowed on him the tongue which *could not lie*. Thomas in vain objected to this inconvenient and involuntary adhesion to veracity, which would make him, as he thought, unfit for church or for market, for king's court or for lady's bower. But all his remonstrances were disregarded by the lady, and Thomas Rymer, whenever the discourse turned on the future, gained the credit of a prophet whether he would or not; for he could say nothing but what was sure to come to pass.

11. Balkis, Queen of Sheba

ONE DAY THERE WAS a gap in the umbrella of birds whose duty it was to fly over the pilgrims to Mecca and shield them from the burning rays of the sun. The peewit had gone on a far journey and had not returned in time to take his place in the feathered ranks. The peewit's behavior annoyed King Solomon, and to placate the great monarch the bird told him a story he had just heard from the lapwing. And he spoke as follows:

The last of the dynasty which ruled Sheba, from which country I have just returned, was Scharabel, a tyrant of such dissolute habits that every father and husband feared him. Now this Scharabel had a vizier so extremely handsome that the daughters of the jinns loved to gaze at him. Indeed, they often transformed themselves into gazelles that they might trot alongside of him as he walked, and feast their eyes upon his masculine beauty. One of these damsels, Umeira by name, conceived for the vizier a violent passion, and, forgetting the great distance which separates the race of the jinns from that of the mortals, she appeared to him one day as he was hunting and offered him her hand on condition that he should fly with her into her own land, and that he should never under any circumstance ask her origin.

The vizier, dazzled by the marvelous beauty of Umeira, gladly yielded, and she transported him to an island in the midst of the ocean, where she married him. At the end of nine months she gave birth to a daughter whom she named Balkis. The vizier, all this while, was ignorant of the true nature of his bride. One fateful day he forgot he had promised her never to ask her origin and queried her as to her race. No sooner had he asked that fatal question than, with a heartbreaking wail of sorrow, she vanished forever from his sight.

The vizier returned with the babe to his native land, and, as she grew to be a great beauty, his greatest fear was that the unchaste Scharabel would see her and carry her off to his harem. In spite of many precautions Scharabel did see her and fall in love with her.

"I had rather see you dead," said her unhappy father, "than in the power of this licentious monster."

"Do not fear for me, father," replied Balkis. "What you dread shall not take place. Appear cheerful before the king. If he wishes to marry me, then ask him to give a splendid wedding."

And the marriage was solemnized with great pomp. After the splendid banquet all the company retired, leaving Balkis alone with the king. There were, however, four female slaves present, one singing, another harping, a third dancing and a fourth pouring out wine for the king. Balkis took the goblet and plied her royal bridegroom well. Suddenly he fell drunk upon the floor, and then with a dagger she stabbed him to the heart.

She immediately told her father what she had done and bade him send orders throughout the town that all the citizens were to bring their daughters before the king that he might choose from them and add the comely ones to his already numerous list of wives and concubines. He obeyed her and the whole town rose in revolt, and rushing furiously to the palace, determined to kill the tyrant Scharabel.

Then Balkis cut off his head and showed it to the excited multitude from the window. A cry of joy rang through Sheba. The palace gates were thrown open and Balkis was chosen queen in the room of the murdered tyrant. And from that hour she has governed the country well, but, alas, like her predecessors she too was a worshiper of the sun.

When Solomon heard the story of the peewit, he wrote a letter and sealed it with his ring, gave it to the bird and bade him carry it immediately to the Queen of Sheba. The peewit flew like an arrow and on the morrow appeared before Balkis and gave her the missive.

The queen read it and was startled at the abrupt and peremptory command at the end, which read, "Do what I bid you: submit immediately to my scepter." She read it to her council, but they did not know what to advise. She then said, "You know what disasters follow on war. This letter is threatening. I will send Solomon a messenger and propitiate him with gifts. If he accepts them, he is not above other kings. If he rejects them, he is a prophet, and we must yield to his sway."

She then dressed five hundred boys as girls and five hundred girls as boys. For presents she collected a thousand carpets of gold and silver tissue, a crown adorned with pearls and diamonds, and a great quantity of perfumes. She also placed a pearl, a diamond bored through spirally and a crystal goblet in a box and gave it to her chief ambassador.

Finally she wrote a letter to Solomon, telling him that if he was a prophet he would be able to distinguish boys from girls in the train of the ambassadors, to guess the contents of the box, pierce the pearl, thread the diamond and fill the goblet with water which came neither from earth nor heaven. To bear the letter she sent the chief nobles of Sheba. "If Solomon receives you with arrogance, fear nothing," she told them. "Pride is a sure token of weakness. If he receives you graciously, be careful—he is a prophet."

The peewit, who had watched all these proceedings and listened to the message and advice, now flew to Solomon and told him all. Solomon immediately ordered his jinns to spread his carpet seven leagues long, leading from his throne towards Sheba. Then he surrounded himself with gold and gems and gathered all his courtiers and officers together, and prepared for an audience.

When the ambassadors set their feet on the carpet, the end of which was beyond the range of vision, they were full of astonishment. This feeling increased to terror when they passed between the ranks of demons, jinns, nobles, princes and soldiers, extending many miles. When the leaders of the embassy reached the foot of the throne, Solomon received them with a gracious smile. Then they presented the queen's letter. Without opening it, Solomon repeated its contents, for it had been read by the peewit. They offered the box, and he said that in it were a pearl, a diamond and a goblet. He next ordered his servants to bring silver ewers before the train of the ambassadors that they might wash their hands after the journey. He picked out the boys from the girls at once, for the boys dipped only their hands in the water whilst the girls tucked up their sleeves to their shoulders and washed arms as well as hands.

Then the box was opened and the pearl produced. Solomon unclasped his pouch and drew forth the magic rock splitter and borer Schamir, applied it to the pearl and a hole was drilled through it at once. Next he took the diamond. The hole bored in it wound about, and a thread inserted in one end would not pass through to the other end. So taking up a piece of silk thread, he called to him a worm, put one end of the thread in its mouth and the worm crawled down the winding perforation and appeared at the other opening with the silk. In gratitude to the little creature Solomon gave it for its food forever the mulberry tree. Then he took the crystal goblet. Summoning a huge Negro slave, he bade him mount a wild horse and gallop it about the plain till it streamed with sweat. With this sweat it was easy to fill the chalice with water that came neither from earth nor heaven.

Having accomplished these tasks, Solomon said to the ambassadors, "Take back your presents; I do not want them. Tell the queen what you have seen and bid her submit to my rule."

When Balkis had heard the report of her servants, she saw that it was in vain for her to resist. Said she, "Solomon is a great prophet, and I myself must do him homage."

So she prepared for her journey and marched to King Solomon at the head of twelve thousand generals and all the armies they commanded. When she was about a league from Jerusalem, the king hit upon a scheme. He called to him a demon and bade him transport immediately from Sheba the throne of the queen and set it beside his own. The jinn replied he would bring it before noon, but the king could not wait, for the queen would soon arrive. Then Asaph, his vizier, said, "Raise thine eyes, sire, to heaven, and before thou canst lower them, the throne of Balkis will be here." Now Asaph knew the ineffable name of God and therefore was able to do what he said. Solomon looked up, and before he looked down Asaph had brought the throne.

As soon as the beautiful and stately Balkis appeared, Solomon asked her if she recognized the seat. She replied, "It is mine, if it is that which it was." This reply charmed Solomon.

Now the jinns were envious of Balkis, and they sought to turn away the heart of Solomon from her. So they told him that she had hairy legs. Consequently Solomon was particularly curious to inspect her legs. He therefore directed the jinns to lay down in front of the throne a pavement of crystal one hundred cubits square. Upon the surface of this he ordered them to spread a little water.

In order to approach Solomon, Queen Balkis raised her petticoats lest they should be wet in passing through what appeared to her to be water of considerable depth. The first step, however, convinced her that the bottom was nearer the surface than she had anticipated. And so she dropped her petticoats, but not before the great king had seen that the jinns had maligned her and that the only blemish on her legs was three goat's hairs. And these hairs he was enabled to remove by a composition of arsenic and lime, which was the first depilatory preparation ever employed. This was one of the five arts introduced by Solomon into the world. The others were the art of taking warm baths, the art of piercing pearls, the art of diving and the art of melting copper.

The queen stepped gracefully towards the king, and, bowing, offered him two wreaths of flowers. One was natural and the other artificial, and she asked him which he preferred. The sagacious king seemed perplexed. He who had written treatises on the herbs, from the cedar to the hyssop, was nearly outwitted. A swarm of bees was buzzing outside a window. He ordered the window to be opened, and the insects flew in. They settled immediately on the wreath of natural flowers, not one approaching the artificial wreath. "I will have the wreath the bees have chosen," said the king triumphantly.

Solomon took Balkis to be his wife, and she worshiped the true God. She gave him all her realm, but he returned it to her. And when she went into her own land, she bore with her the fruit of her union with Solomon, and in the course of time brought forth a son, who is the ancestor of the kings of Abyssinia.

◈◈◈

12. The Girl Who Was Half-Married

SUMMONING HIS SON to his bedside, a great nobleman, wise, prudent and virtuous, spoke these words: "My dear son, I have left you all my worldly goods and wish you to listen to the last words of advice I shall ever be able to give you, for I am departing this life. Heed these three maxims: Never come to your neighbor's table so often that he dares to set brown bread before you. Never race your horse downhill, and never wed a woman of a foreign country. If you forget these sayings or ignore their teaching, you will regret it."

Now the son was good, and thanking his father for his counsel, he promised he would endeavor never to forget or act contrary to these maxims. Soon after this his father died and was buried in a manner befitting a nobleman of his high rank.

Without father and mother, for she also had left this world, there was not much to keep the young gentleman at home. Besides, he was as yet unmarried and fond of the society of ladies. So the days he did not go hunting, he spent visiting. The gentlefolk of the neighborhood saw much of him, and he especially enjoyed visiting the hostel of a gentleman who had married a wife who was a great beauty. Indeed, the young man came there so often that his host became jealous, supposing that his guest had fallen in love with his wife and fearing that she might be tempted to forget her duty to her husband. As he felt it would be unwise to go to the young man and tell him frankly what he thought, he decided to change little by little his manner of entertaining him. If this were done, he believed his guest, if he was not altogether stupid, would take the hint and realize that his too-frequent visiting was not wholly pleasing to his host. So one day instead of white bread he had brown bread set before the young man, who after a while noticed it. Immediately his father's first maxim flashed into his mind and he understood he had done wrong by coming here so often. He regretted his fault very much. Hiding in his sleeve a slice of the brown bread, he carried it home and hung it up by a string in the parlor as a memento. Thereafter his visits to his jealous neighbor and his pretty wife were quite infrequent.

One day when his greyhounds were chasing a hare, he rode his horse at a headlong pace down a hill after his dogs and their quarry. At the bottom of the hill the horse stumbled, fell and broke his neck. But his rider escaped serious injury, and for this good luck he was duly grateful. As he held up the hare, which had been caught, and then gazed on the poor horse he had been so fond of, he suddenly remembered his father's second maxim. And he said to himself, "If I had only thought of it in time, I would have avoided this accident and my horse would still be alive and breathing." On his return he hung up the horse's hide next to the brown bread.

Some time later a great desire to travel and see foreign countries came over him. So he sailed the seas and crossed mountains and visited many foreign lands. In the most distant one he struck a warm friendship with a grand seigneur and was invited to be a guest in his hostel. And this seigneur was so pleased with the stranger's person and refined manners that he offered him the hand of his beautiful daughter in marriage, and this without knowing anything about his origin or condition. So the young man became engaged to the seigneur's daughter, and the wedding day was announced. Naturally his expectation was that after the marriage ceremony and the feasting and dancing, he would retire with his bride and spend the night with her. However, this was not the custom in this strange land. It was explained to him that the grooms had to wait until the second night to sleep with their brides. He begged that an exception might be made in his case, but this, they said, could not be done.

After the dancing was finished, his bride was led into one chamber and he into the one next to it. Discovering that the wall between was made of clay, with his sword he pierced a hole in it, and, looking through, he saw his bride lying in bed. In a moment the chaplain of the hostel entered the room and got into bed with her. No doubt the holy man wished to keep her company so she would not become lonesome or be afraid. Or perhaps, like certain Cordeliers in France, he took this pleasant method of collecting the tithe. This surprising business made the young traveler realize that some flies had got into his cream and that his situation was both embarrassing and ridiculous. Immediately his father's third maxim came to mind. Oh, why had he let it slip his memory? But he consoled himself with the thought that perhaps things had not gone so far that he could not extricate himself without being too badly scathed.

Next morning the good chaplain, his predecessor and substitute for one night, arose and hurried from the room, forgetting to take his breeches with him. The young gentleman, having observed the priest's oversight, came into the bride's chamber and greeted her graciously. Seizing a favorable opportunity, he picked up the clergyman's breeks from under the bed without being seen and withdrew.

That day he was careful to conceal his discontent. He acted the part of a happy bridegroom. When evening came his bride went to her bed, which had been adorned and richly dressed for the occasion. Soon after, the groom was told he could now join her. But he refused to enter her room and gave reasons.

"You do not know who or what I am," he said to the girl's parents. "In giving me your daughter without first seeking this knowledge, you have paid me a high compliment and I thank you. However, I have solemnly resolved never to sleep with her until I have shown her and you who I am, the property I own and the hostel I live in."

"Your many shining virtues," said the father, who was beginning to feel uneasy, "show that you are a nobleman of high rank. We are fully satisfied with you. Therefore, do not hesitate to consummate your marriage. There is no cause for delay. Later on, if we wish, we can find out who you are." But the young man was unyielding. He vowed he would never bed his bride until she and her parents came to his country and visited him at his hostel.

So he returned to his native land. When he arrived, he hung up the priest's breeches beside the brown bread and the horse's hide. Then he set everything in order and made preparations to entertain the foreign seigneur's daughter and those who were accompanying her. When they arrived, they were greeted hospitably and entertained in a most splendid fashion. Their host wined and dined them handsomely. They were greatly pleased, and the splendid appointments of his hostel amazed them. The seigneur was delighted to have married his daughter to such a fine gentleman.

When they saw the brown bread, the horse's hide and the priest's breeches, they asked their host what this strange exhibit meant. Thereupon he related how his father had given him the three maxims and how by failing to heed them he had got into trouble.

"By forgetting the first maxim," he said, "I made a husband jealous, and he placed brown bread before me to make me realize that I visited his house too often. So I lost a dear friend. By forgetting the second, I killed my favorite steed. By forgetting the third, I contracted a marriage that turned into a farce. As you know I was not permitted to spend the wedding night with my bride. As the wall separating me from her was not very strong, I pierced a hole in it and saw your chaplain in the place I should have occupied. The next morning I picked up the breeches which he left under the bed. There they hang to remind me of the wisdom of my father's third maxim, never wed a woman of a foreign country.

"I am not a man to take the leavings of a priest, and I thank God that I am not so obligated to your daughter that she cannot part from me. So carry her back with you to your country. But, since I have caused you to make such a far journey, I wish to pay all your expenses."

This speech so surprised the foreign seigneur that he became utterly confused. Neither he nor any of the girl's kinsfolk knew what to say. What could they do? To try force would have been foolish, for they were among strangers. So they took the expense money and returned to their native land.

᪥᪥᪥

13. Nothing Like Stark Dead

THERE WAS of old time a cobbler in the city of Orfa. One day he saw a dervish passing, the seams of whose shoes had given way. The cobbler said, "Dervish, come, sit down till I sew up the seams of thy shoes and patch the holes." The dervish answered, "If thou hast a remedy, apply it to the hole in my heart." The cobbler gave him his right hand and he came and sat down; and the cobbler gave him food to eat and sewed up the holes in his shoes and said, "O dervish, I too wish to journey; what counsel dost thou give me?" The dervish answered, "I have three counsels; see thou keep them. My first is this: set not out on the journey till thou hast found a good fellow traveler, for the Apostle of God hath said, 'The companion, then the road.' My second is this: light not in a waterless place. My third is this: enter great cities when the sun is rising." Then he went his way.

After some days the cobbler found some suitable fellow travelers and set out. While they were on the road, one day in the afternoon a city appeared before them. The cobbler youth asked, "What city is this city?" The companions answered, "It is the city of Aleppo." The youth said, "Today it is near evening; I shall not enter the city today." Howsoever the companions urged him, it was no use; so at length they left him and went on.

The youth went and lighted on the bank of a stream and

remained there that night. Now there were tombs near the youth; and when it was midnight he saw two men coming from the city carrying something which they laid in the grave-yard, and then they went away. Then the youth went up to that grave, and, striking a light with a flint and steel, lit a candle. He saw that they had laid there a new coffin, and from the four sides of that coffin streams of blood were running. The cobbler youth opened the lid of the coffin and looked to see what he might see. There was a body bathed in blood; the garments were of massive gold embroidery, and on the finger was a ring in which a stone glittered. The youth coveted the ring and took hold of it that he might pull it off, whereupon the body raised its head and said, "O youth, fearest thou not God that thou wouldst take my ring?"

Then the youth saw that it was a girl like the moon of four-teen nights, a torment of the age, like a lovely rose; and he said, "What is this plight?"

The girl said, "Now is not the time for questions. If thou be able, relieve me; and afterward I will help thine affairs."

Straightway the youth pulled off his outer robe and tore it in pieces and bound up the girl's wounds and laid her in a place. When it was morning he took her on his back and brought her into the city and placed her in a cell in a certain place; and to all who asked of her he said, "She is my sister; passion came upon me and I brought this plight upon this poor creature, and she innocent." The youth tended the girl's wounds, and in the course of a month or two she became well.

One day she went to the bath, and when she returned she asked the youth for inkhorn, reed and paper. The youth brought them and placed them before her. The girl wrote a letter and gave it into the youth's hands; and therein was written thus: "Thou who art Khoja Dibab, the superintendent of the bazaar, give the bearer of this letter a hundred sequins and send him to me. Disclose nothing to my father of my health or my death. If thou do, thou shalt reflect well upon the issue." She sealed it and said, "Go, give this letter to a khoja who sits in such and such a place in the bazaar, and take whatever he gives thee and bring it."

The youth took that letter and went to the bazaar and asked, and they showed him to him, and he gave the letter into his hand. When the khoja opened the letter and read it, he kissed it and raised it to his head, and straightway drew forth a purse of gold and gave it to the youth. The youth brought it and laid it before the girl. She said, "Go, take a house and buy with what is over clothes for thee and me." The youth went and took a house and bought sumptuous clothes and brought them to the girl. And they arose and went to that house which they had taken.

Again she wrote a letter which she gave to the youth, who took it to the khoja, who this time gave him two purses, which he took to the girl. She said to him, "Go, my youth, and buy some provisions and furniture for the house." And the youth went and bought them. Then the girl got another purse of sequins, and she said to the youth, "Go, buy thyself horses and arms and male slaves and female slaves." And the youth went and bought them, and he brought them and gave them to the girl.

"Now tell me what are these matters," said he.

"Now is not the time; by and by," she answered.

Gradually the girl built palaces there and increased the number of her male slaves and female slaves, and whenever she gave the youth a letter he went and got two or three purses of gold from that khoja. One day she gave the youth a purse of gold and said, "In the bazaar is a young man they call Ghazanfer Agha. Now go and find him and ask of him some precious stuff, and he will show it thee, and whatever price he asks for it, give him the double thereof, and take and bring it." So the youth went and found him, and sat awhile and talked with him. And whatever the price of it was, he gave the double, and took the stuff. Ghazanfer Agha marveled at this. The youth returned and gave it to the girl, and again asked of these matters, but the girl said that this was not yet the time for that.

And she took out a purse of jewels and gave it to the young cobbler and said, "Take these jewels and go to Ghazanfer Agha and ask him to put a value on them, and take them out and lay them before him and see what he will say to thee. And when putting the jewels back into the purse, present him with three of them." So she sent him off. The youth said, "I shall go, but when I come back tell me the things that have befallen thee."

He went and did as the girl had said. When Ghazanfer Agha saw these gifts, he said to the youth, "O youth, thou hast made us ashamed. Pray be troubled to come once to our house and honor us that we may show our affection." The youth replied, "What though it be so; tomorrow I shall come." And he bade him farewell and he came and told the girl, and she said, "Go tomorrow; but when thou enterest his house look not to this side nor that side, but look straight before thee." And thus did she warn him.

When it was morning the youth arose; and Ghazanfer Agha looked and saw the youth coming and he said, "Welcome!" and took him and led him to his house. And the youth looked at nothing, but passed on and sat down. And Ghazanfer Agha treated and entertained that youth with all manner of delicious foods, and then sent him away. And the youth came and told the girl, and she said, "Go again tomorrow and talk with him, and when thou riseth, do thou too invite him; and be not jealous." And the youth reflected and said in his heart, "This Ghazanfer Agha must be the friend of this girl; anyhow we shall see; whatever God does He does well."

In the morning he went and invited him, and then came to the girl and gave her word and said, "Tell me and let me hear of the matters of that night." The girl answered, "Now is not the time; go and get these things which are needful." The youth went and got them and brought them and gave her them and said, "Lo, I have brought them; tell me." The girl said, "Now is the guest coming; it cannot be; by and by I will tell thee."

When Ghazanfer Agha came, the youth gave the girl word and she said, "Go and meet him and lead him and bring him here." The youth said in his heart, "This is not without reason; but wait, we shall see." And he led him respectfully, and he entered and sat down with the girl. As her veil hid her face, all but the eyes, he did not recognize her. The food was served and they ate and drank and made merry till the evening. Then the girl sent word and the youth came in, and she said, "Take care, be it not that thou lettest Ghazanfer Agha leave this evening." And the youth said, "What is this of thee that thou dost not dismiss him?" The girl answered, "I will tell thee afterward." The youth said in his heart, "I shall slay the two of you this night." And he went out.

When it was night Ghazanfer Agha asked leave to go away, but the youth would not let him, and the guest saw that it was not to be, so he remained; and they brought out a clean coverlet and mattress and made a bed for him.

And he lay down, and the youth lay down with the girl, but he slept not that he might watch the girl. When it was midnight the girl arose and the youth saw her, but he made no sound, and the girl went close to Ghazanfer Agha. The youth, unable to endure it any longer, rose from his place and said fiercely to the girl, "What seekest thou there?" She saw that the youth spake angrily and she took him by the hand and drew him to a place apart and said, "I am about to slay this Ghazanfer Agha." The youth said, "What is the reason of it?"

"The reason of it is this," she replied. "I am the daughter of the king of this land, and this youth was a butcher's apprentice. One day when going to the bath I met this youth selling meat upon the road. As soon as I saw him, I fell in love with him, and the bird, my heart, was taken, so that I was without rest and could not remain quiet. I saw there was no help for it, so I got him by force of money, and sometimes I went to his house and sometimes I had him brought in disguise to my palace. One night I went in disguise to his house, and I saw him sitting conversing with a gypsy harlot, and I got angry and cursed the two of them. This fellow was wont to use the dagger, and he gave me many wounds, and thought me dead and put me in a coffin and sent me with two men who laid me in that tomb thou sawest. Praise be to God! my time was not yet. Thou didst come to me like Khizr. Now do thou kill him."

The youth said, "I shall kill him. Wilt thou marry me according to the Ordinance of God?" She answered, "I will not marry thee, but the vizier has a daughter fairer than I. Her will I get for thee."

Then the youth smote him and killed him. The girl said, "In the morning go to my father and give him good news. And go tonight and bring here all the possessions of this fellow."

The youth said, "Tomorrow thy father's servants will bring them."

When it was morning the youth went and gave the good news to the king. And the king sent slave girls who brought the girl to the palace. And her mother was glad when she saw her safe and sound. And they confiscated the property of Ghazanfer Agha and bestowed it on the cobbler youth. But what would he do with the wealth? His desire was the girl.

The king's viziers said, "My king, it were right if thou give the girl to the youth." The king answered, "It is my desire too; for when my daughter disappeared and we sought but could not find her, I made a promise, saying that to him who brought good news of my daughter I should give her. But the girl does not wish it." The viziers said, "My king, our daughters are thine; make the youth thy client; whichever girl thou pleasest, give her to him."

The king said, "I shall make a proposal"; and he went and spake with her mother. And the girl's mother went to her and with difficulty persuaded her; and then sent word to the king. That hour they performed the marriage ceremony, and the king made the youth a vizier; and they lived for a long time in joyance and delight.

❦❦❦ ❦❦❦

14. *Women in Love*

ONCE ON A TIME there were three brothers. I don't quite know how it happened, but each of them had got the right to wish one thing, whatever he chose. So the two elder were not long a-thinking; they wished that every time they put their hands in their pockets they might pull out a piece of money; for they said, "The man who has as much money as he wishes for is always sure to get on in the world."

But the youngest wished something better still. He wished that every woman he saw might fall in love with him as soon as she saw him. And you shall soon hear how far better this was than gold and goods.

So, when they had all wished their wishes, the two elder were for setting out to see the world; and Boots, their youngest brother, asked if he mightn't go along with them, but they wouldn't hear of such a thing. "Wherever we go," they said, "we shall be treated as counts and kings; but you, you starveling wretch, who haven't a penny, and never will have one, who do you think will care a bit about you?"

"Well, but in spite of that, I'd like to go with you," said Boots. "Perhaps a dainty bit may fall to my share too off the plates of such high and mighty lords."

At last, after begging and praying, he got leave to go with them, if he would be their servant, else they wouldn't hear of it.

So, when they had gone a day or so, they came to an inn, where the two had the money alighted and called for fish and flesh, and fowl, and brandy and mead, and everything that was good; but Boots, poor fellow, had to look after their luggage and all that belonged to the two great people. Now, as he went to and fro outside, and loitered about in the innyard, the innkeeper's wife looked out of window and saw the servant of the gentlemen upstairs; and, all at once, she thought she had never set eyes on such a handsome chap. So she stared and stared, and the longer she looked the handsomer he seemed.

"Why what, by the Deil's skin and bones, is it that you are standing there gaping at out of the window?" said her husband. "I think 'twould be better if you just looked how the sucking pig is getting on, instead of hanging out of window in that way. Don't you know what grand folk we have in the house today?"

"Oh!" said his old dame, "I don't care a farthing about such a pack of rubbish. If they don't like it, they may lump it and be off. But just do come and look at this lad out in the yard. So handsome a fellow I never saw in all my born days; and if you'll do as I wish, we'll ask him to step in and treat him a little, for, poor lad, he seems to have a hard fight of it."

"Have you lost the little brains you had, Goody?" said the husband, whose eyes glistened with rage. "Into the kitchen with you and mind the fire, but don't stand there glowering after strange men."

So the wife had nothing left for it but to go into the kitchen and look after the cooking. As for the lad outside, she couldn't get leave to ask him in, or to treat him either. But just as she was about spitting the pig in the kitchen, she made an excuse for running out into the yard, and then and there she gave Boots a pair of scissors, of such a kind that they cut of themselves out of the air the loveliest clothes anyone ever saw, silk and satin, and all that was fine. "This you shall have because you are so handsome," said the innkeeper's wife.

So when the two elder brothers had crammed themselves with roast and boiled, they wished to be off again, and Boots had to stand behind their carriage and be their servant. And so they traveled a good way, till they came to another inn. There the two brothers again alighted and went indoors, but

Boots, who had no money, they wouldn't have inside with them. No, he must wait outside and watch the luggage. "And mind," they said, "if anyone asks whose servant you are, say we are two foreign princes."

But the same thing happened now as happened before. While Boots stood hanging about out in the yard, the innkeeper's wife came to the window and saw him, and she too fell in love with him, just like the first innkeeper's wife. And there she stood and stared, for she thought she could never have her fill of looking at him. Then her husband came running through the room with something the two princes had ordered.

"Don't stand there staring like a cow at a barn door but take this into the kitchen, and look after your fish kettle, Goody," said the man. "Don't you see what grand people we have in the house today?"

"I don't care a farthing for such a pack of rubbish," said the wife. "If they don't like what they get, they may lump it and eat what they brought with them. But just do come here and see what you shall see! Such a handsome fellow as walks here, out in the yard, I never saw in all my born days. Shan't we ask him in and treat him a little? He looks as if he needed it, poor chap. Such a love! Such a love!"

"You never had much wit, and the little you had is clean gone, I can see," said the man, who was much more angry than the first innkeeper and chased his wife back, neck and crop, into the kitchen. "Into the kitchen with you and don't stand glowering after lads," he said.

So she had to go in and mind her fish kettle, and she dared not treat Boots, for she was afraid of her old man. But, as she stood there making up the fire, she made an excuse for running out into the yard, and then and there she gave Boots a table-cloth, which was such that it covered itself with the best dishes you could think of, as soon as it was spread out. "This you shall have," she said, "because you're so handsome."

So when the two brothers had eaten and drunk of all that was in the house and had paid the bill in hard cash, they set off again, and Boots stood up behind their carriage. But when they had gone so far that they grew hungry again, they turned into a third inn and called for the best and dearest they could think of. "For," said they, "we are two kings on our travels, and as for our money, it grows like grass."

Well, when the innkeeper heard that, there was such a roasting and baking and boiling; why! you might smell the dinner at the next neighbor's house, though it wasn't so very near. And the innkeeper was at his wit's end to find all he wished to put before the two kings. But Boots, he had to stand outside here too and look after the things in the carriage.

So it was the same story over again. The innkeeper's wife came to the window and peeped out, and there she saw the servant standing by the carriage. Such a handsome chap she had never set eyes upon before; so she looked and looked, and the more she stared the handsomer he seemed to the inn-keeper's wife. Then out came the innkeeper, scampering through the room with some dainty the traveling kings had ordered, and he wasn't very soft-tongued when he saw his old dame standing and glowering out of the window. "Don't you know better than to stand gaping and staring there when we have such great folk in the house?" he said. "Back into the kitchen with you this minute, to your custards."

"Well! well!" she said, "as for them, I don't care a pin. If they can't wait till the custards are baked, they may go without—that's all. But do, pray, come here and you'll see such a lovely lad standing out here in the yard. Why I never saw such a pretty fellow in my life. Shan't we ask him in now and treat him a little, for he looks as if it would do him good. Oh! what a darling! What a darling!"

"A wanton gadabout you've been all your days and so you are still," said her husband, who was in such a rage he scarce knew which leg to stand on. "But if you don't be off to your custards this minute, I'll soon find out how to make you stir your stumps; see if I don't."

So the wife had off to her custards as fast as she could, for she knew that her husband would stand no nonsense. But as she stood there over the fire, she stole out into the yard and gave Boots a tap.

"If you only turn this tap," she said, "you'll get the finest drink of whatever kind you choose, both mead and wine and brandy. And this you shall have because you are so handsome."

So when the two brothers had eaten and drunk all they could, they started from the inn, and Boots stood up behind again as their servant, and thus they drove far and wide till they came to a king's palace. There the two elder gave themselves out for two emperor's sons, and, as they had plenty of money and were so fine that their clothes shone again ever so far off, they were well treated. They had rooms in the palace, and the king couldn't tell how to make enough of them. But Boots, who went about in the same rags he stood in when he left home, and who had never a penny in his pocket, he was taken up by the king's guard and put across to an island, whither they used to row over all the beggars and rogues that came to the palace. This the king had ordered because he wouldn't have the mirth at the palace spoilt by those dirty blackguards. And thither too only just as much food as would keep body and soul together was sent over every day. Now Boot's brothers saw very well that the guard was rowing him over to the island, but they were glad to be rid of him and didn't pay the least heed to him.

But when Boots got over there, he just pulled out his scissors and began to snip and cut in the air. So the scissors cut out the finest clothes anyone would wish to see, silk and satin both; and all the beggars on the island were soon dressed far finer than the king and all his guests in the palace. After that Boots pulled out his tablecloth and spread it out, and so they got food too, the poor beggars. Such a feast had never been seen at the king's palace as was served that day at the beggars' isle.

"Thirsty, too, I'll be bound you all are," said Boots, and out with his tap, gave it a turn, and so the beggars got all a drop to drink; and such ale and mead the king himself had never tasted in all his life.

So next morning when those who were to bring the beggars their food on the island came rowing over with the scrapings of the porridge pots and cheese parings—that was what the poor wretches had—the beggars wouldn't so much as taste them, and the king's men fell to wondering what it could mean. But they wondered much more when they got a good look at the beggars, for they were so fine the guard thought they must be emperors or popes at least, and that they must have rowed to a wrong island; but when they looked better about them, they saw they were come to the old place.

Then they soon found out it must be he whom they had rowed out the day before who had brought the beggars on the island all this state and bravery; and, as soon as they got back to the palace, they were not slow to tell how the man whom they had rowed over the day before had dressed out all the beggars so fine and grand that precious things fell from their clothes. "And as for the porridge and cheese we took, they wouldn't even taste them, so proud have they got," they said.

One of them, too, had smelt out that the lad had a pair of scissors which he cut out the clothes with. "When he only snips with those scissors up in the air, he snips and cuts out nothing but silk and satin," said he.

So when the princess heard that, she had neither peace nor rest till she saw the lad and his scissors that cut out silk and satin from the air. Such a pair was worth having, she thought, for with its help she would soon get all the finery she wished for. Well, she begged the king so long and hard he was forced to send a messenger for the lad who owned the scissors; and when he came to the palace, the princess asked him if it were true that he had such and such a pair of scissors, and if he would sell it to her. Yes, it was all true he had such a pair, said Boots, but sell it he wouldn't. And with that he took the scissors out of his pocket and snipped and snipped with them in the air till strips of silk and satin flew all about him.

"Nay, but you must sell me these scissors," said the princess. "You may ask what you please for them, but have them I must."

No! Such a pair of scissors he wouldn't sell at any price, for he could never get such a pair again. And while they stood and haggled for the scissors, the princess had time to look better at Boots, and she too thought with the innkeepers' wives that she had never seen such a handsome fellow before. So she began to bargain for the scissors over again and begged and prayed Boots to let her have them. He might ask many,

many hundred dollars for them, 'twas all the same to her, so she got them.

"No! sell them I won't," said Boots, "but all the same, if I can get leave to sleep one night on the floor of the princess' bedroom, close by the door, I'll give her the scissors. I'll do her no harm, but if she's afraid, she may have two men to watch inside the room."

Yes! the princess was glad enough to give him leave, for she was ready to grant him anything if she only got the scissors. So Boots lay on the floor inside the princess' bedroom that night, and two men stood watch there too. But the princess didn't get much rest after all! for when she ought to have been asleep, she must open her eyes to look at Boots, and so it went on the whole night. If she shut her eyes for a minute, she peeped out at him again the next, such a handsome fellow he seemed to her to be.

Next morning Boots was rowed over to the beggars' isle again; but when they came with the porridge scrapings and cheese parings from the palace, there was no one who would taste them that day either, and so those who brought the food were more astonished than ever. But one of those who brought the food contrived to smell out that the lad who owned the scissors owned also a tablecloth which he only needed to spread out and it was covered with all the good things he could wish for. So when he got back to the palace, he wasn't long before he said, "Such hot joints and such custards I never saw the like of it in the king's palace."

And when the princess heard that, she told it to the king, and begged and prayed so long that he was forced to send a messenger out to the island to fetch the lad who owned the tablecloth. And so Boots came back to the palace. The princess

must and would have the cloth of him and offered him gold
and green woods for it, but Boots wouldn't sell it at any price.

"But if I may have leave to lie on the bench by the princess'
bedside tonight, she shall have the cloth. But if she's afraid,
she is welcome to set four men to watch inside the room."

Yes! the princess agreed to this, so Boots lay down on the
bench by the bedside, and the four men watched. But if the
princess hadn't much sleep the night before, she had much less
this, for she could scarce get a wink of sleep. There she lay
wide awake looking at the lovely lad the whole night through,
and after all, the night seemed too short.

Next morning Boots was rowed off again to the beggars'
island, though sorely against the princess' will, so happy was
she to be near him. But it was past praying for; to the island
he must go, and there was an end of it. But when those who
brought the food to the beggars came with the porridge scrapings and cheese parings, there wasn't one of them who would
even look at what the king sent, and those who brought it
didn't wonder either; though they all thought it strange that
none of them was thirsty. But just then one of the king's guard
smelled out that the lad who had owned the scissors and the
tablecloth had a tap besides, which, if one only turned it a
little, gave out the rarest drink, both ale and mead and wine.
So when he came back to the palace, he couldn't keep his
mouth shut this time any more than before; he went about
telling high and low about the tap, and how easy it was to
draw all sorts of drink out of it. "And as for that mead and ale,
I've never tasted the like of them in the king's palace; honey
and syrup are nothing to them for sweetness."

So when the princess heard that, she was all for getting the
tap and was nothing loath to strike a bargain with the owner

either. So she went again to the king and begged him to send a messenger to the beggars' isle after the lad who had owned the scissors and cloth, for now he had another thing worth having, she said. And when the king heard it was a tap that was good to give the best ale and wine anyone could drink, when one gave it a turn, he wasn't long in sending the messenger, I should think.

So when Boots came up to the palace, the princess asked whether it were true he had a tap which could do such and such things? Yes! he had such a tap in his waistcoat pocket. But when the princess wished with all her might to buy it, Boots said, as he had said twice before, he wouldn't sell it, even if the princess bade half the kingdom for it. "But all the same," said Boots, "if I may have leave to sleep on your bed tonight, outside the quilt, you shall have my tap. I'll not do you any harm; but, if you are afraid, you may set eight men to watch in your room."

"Oh, no!" said the princess. "There is no need of that; I know you so well now." And so Boots lay outside the princess' bed that night. But if she hadn't slept much the two nights before, she had less sleep that night. She couldn't shut her eyes the livelong night but lay and looked at Boots, who lay alongside her outside the quilt.

So, when she got up in the morning and they were going to row Boots back to the island, she begged them to hold hard a little bit. And in she ran to the king and begged him so prettily to let her have Boots for a husband, she was so fond of him, and unless she had him she did not care to live.

"Well, well!" said the king. "You shall have him if you must; for he who has such things is just as rich as you are."

So Boots got the princess and half the kingdom—the other

half he was to have when the king died. And so everything went smooth and well. But as for his brothers, who had always been so bad to him, he packed them off to the beggars' island.

"There," said Boots, "perhaps they may find out which is best off, the man who has his pockets full of money, or the man whom all women fall in love with." Nor, to tell you the truth, do I think it would help them much to wander about upon the beggars' island pulling pieces of money out of their pockets. And so, if Boots hasn't taken them off the island, there they are still walking about to this very day, eating cheese parings and the scrapings of the porridge pots.

15. *The Hasty Word*

IN A CERTAIN VILLAGE there lived an old couple in great poverty, and they had one son. The son grew up and the old woman began to say to the old man, "It's time for us to get our son married." "Well then, go and ask for a wife for him," said he.

So she went to a neighbor to ask for his daughter for her son; the neighbor refused. She went to a second peasant's, but the second refused too—to a third, but he showed her the door. She went round the whole village; not a soul would grant her request. So she returned home and cried, "Well, old man! our lad's an unlucky fellow!"

"How so?"

"I've trudged round to every house, but no one will give him his daughter."

"That's a bad business!" says the old man. "The summer will soon be coming, but we have no one to work for us here. Go to another village, old woman, perhaps you will get a bride for him there."

The old woman went to another village, visited every house from one end to the other, but there wasn't an atom of good to be got out of it. Wherever she thrusts herself, they always refuse. With what she left home, with that she returned home. "No," she says, "no one wants to become related to us poor beggars."

"If that's the case," answers the old man, "there's no use in wearing out your legs. Jump up on to the *polati* (the sleeping place)."

The son was sorely afflicted and began to entreat his parents, saying, "My born father and my born mother! give me your blessing. I will go and seek my fate myself."

"But where will you go?"

"Where my eyes lead me."

So they gave him their blessing and let him go whithersoever it pleased him. Well, the youth went out upon the highway, began to weep very bitterly, and said to himself as he walked, "Was I born into the world worse than all other men, that not a single girl is willing to marry me? Methinks if the devil himself would give me a bride, I'd take even her!" Suddenly, as if rising from the earth, there appeared before him a very old man.

"Good day, good youth!"

"Good day, old man!"

"What was that you were saying just now?"

The youth was frightened and did not know what reply to make.

"Don't be afraid of me! I shan't do you any harm, and moreover, perhaps I may get you out of your trouble. Speak boldly!"

The youth told him everything precisely. "Poor creature that I am! There isn't a single girl who will marry me. Well, as I went along I became exceedingly wretched and in my misery I said, 'If the devil offered me a bride, I'd take even her!' "

The old man laughed and said, "Follow me, I'll let you choose a lovely bride for yourself."

By-and-by they reached a lake. "Turn your back to the lake and walk backwards," said the old man. Scarcely had the youth had time to turn around and take a couple of steps when he found himself under the water and in a white stone palace —all its rooms splendidly furnished, cunningly decorated. The old man gave him to eat and to drink. Afterwards he introduced twelve maidens, each one more beautiful than the other. "Choose whichever you like! Whichever you choose, her will I bestow upon you."

"That's a puzzling job!" said the youth. "Give me till tomorrow morning to think about it, grandfather!"

"Well, think away!" said the old man, and led his guest to a private chamber. The youth lay down to sleep and thought, "Which one shall I choose?" Suddenly the door opened; a beautiful maiden entered. "Are you asleep, or not, good youth?" says she.

"No, fair maiden! I can't get to sleep, for I'm always thinking which bride to choose."

"That's the very reason I have come to give you counsel. You see, good youth, you've managed to become the devil's guest. Now listen. If you want to go on living in the white world, then do what I tell you. But if you don't follow my instructions, you'll never get out of here alive!"

"Tell me what to do, fair maiden. I won't forget it all my life."

"Tomorrow the fiend will bring you the twelve maidens, each one exactly like the others. But you take a good look and choose me. A fly will be sitting above my right eye—that will be a certain guide for you." And then the fair maiden proceeded to tell him about herself, who she was.

"Do you know the priest of such and such a village?" she says. "I'm his daughter, the one who disappeared from home when nine years old. One day my father was angry with me and in his wrath he said, 'May devils fly away with you!' I went out on the steps and began to cry. All of a sudden the fiends seized me and brought me here; and here I am living with them!"

Next morning the old man brought in the twelve fair maidens—one just like another—and ordered the youth to choose his bride. He looked at them and took her above whose right eye sat a fly. The old man was loath to give her up, so he shifted the maidens about and told him to make a fresh choice. The youth pointed out the same one as before. The fiend obliged him to choose yet a third time. He again guessed his bride aright.

"Well, you're in luck! Take her home with you," said the fiend.

Immediately the youth and the fair maiden found themselves on the shore of the lake, and until they reached the high road they kept on walking backwards. Presently the devils came rushing after them in hot pursuit. "Let us recover our maiden!" they cry.

They look; there are no footsteps going away from the lake; all the footsteps lead into the water! They ran to and fro, they searched everywhere, but they had to go back empty-handed.

Well, the good youth brought his bride to her village and stopped opposite the priest's house. The priest saw him and sent out his laborer, saying, "Go and ask who those people are."

"We? We're travelers; please let us spend the night in your house," they replied.

"I have merchants paying me a visit," says the priest, "and even without them there's but little room in the house."

"What are you thinking of, father?" says one of the merchants. "It's always one's duty to accommodate a traveler; they won't interfere with us."

"Very well, let them come in."

So they came in, exchanged greetings and sat down on a bench in the back corner.

"Don't you know me, father?" presently asks the fair maiden. "Of a surety I am your own daughter."

Then she told him everything that had happened. They began to kiss and embrace each other, to pour forth tears of joy. "And who is this man?" says the priest.

"That is my betrothed. He brought me back into the white world; if it hadn't been for him I should have remained down there forever!"

After this the fair maiden untied her bundle, and in it were gold and silver dishes. She had carried them off from the devils. The merchant looked at them and said, "Ah! those are my dishes. One day I was feasting with my guests, and when

I got drunk I became angry with my wife. 'To the devil with you!' I exclaimed, and began flinging from the table and beyond the threshold whatever I could lay my hands upon. At that moment my dishes disappeared!"

And in reality so had it happened. When the merchant mentioned the devil's name, the fiend immediately appeared at the threshold, began seizing the gold and silver wares and flinging in their place bits of pottery.

Well, by this accident the youth got himself a capital bride. And after he had married her, he went back to his parents. They had long ago counted him as lost to them forever. And indeed it was no subject for jesting; he had been away from home three whole years, and yet it seemed to him that he had not in all spent more than twenty-four hours with the devils.

16. *The Bailie of London*

THERE WERE at some time of the world two brothers in one farm, and they were very great friends, and they had each a son. And one of the brothers died, and he left his brother guardian of his son. When the lad was near to be grown up, he was keeping the farm for his mother almost as well as his father could have done. One night he saw a dream in his sleep, the most beautiful lady that there was in the world, and he dreamed of her three times, and he resolved to marry her and no other woman in the world. And he would not stay in the farm, and he grew pale, and his father's brother could not think what ailed him; and he was always asking him what was wrong with him.

"Well, never mind," one day he said, "brother of my father. I have seen a dream, the most beautiful woman that there is in the world, and I will marry no other but her; and I will now go out and search for her over the whole world till I find her."

Said the uncle, "Son of my brother, I have a hundred pounds. I will give them to thee, and go; and when that is spent come back to me and I will give thee another hundred."

So the lad took the hundred pounds, and he went to France, and then he went to Spain, and all over the world, but he could not find the lady he had seen in his sleep. At last he came to London, and he had spent all his money and his clothes were worn, and he did not know what he should do for a night's lodging.

Well, as he was wandering about the streets, whom should he see but a quiet-looking respectable old woman; and he spoke to her; and from less to more, he told her all that had happened to him. And she was well pleased to see a country-man, and she said, "I am a Highland woman, though I am in this town." And she took him to a small house that she had, and she gave him meat and clothes. And she said, "Go out now and take a walk; maybe thou mayest see here in one day what thou mightest not see in a year."

On the next day he was out taking a walk about the town, and he saw a woman at a window, and he knew her at once, for she was the lady he had seen in his sleep, and he went back to the old woman.

"How went it with thee this day, Gael?" said she.

"It went well," said he. "Oh, I have seen the lady I saw in my sleep." And he told her all about it.

Then the old lady asked about the house and the street; and when she knew, "Thou hast seen her," said she. "That is all thou wilt see of her. That is the daughter of the Bailie of London. But I am her foster mother, and I would be right glad if she would marry a countryman of my own. Now, do thou go out on the morrow, and I will give thee fine Highland clothes, and thou wilt find the lady walking in such a street. Herself and three maidens of company will go out together. Do thou tread on her gown; and when she turns round to see what is the matter, do thou speak to her."

Well, the lad did this. He went out and he found the lady, and he set his foot on her dress, and the gown rent from the band; and when she turned round he said, "I am asking you much grace—it was an accident."

"It was not your fault; it was the fault of the dressmaker that made the dress so long," said she.

And she looked at him; and when she saw how handsome he was, she said, "Will you be so kind as to come home with me to my father's house and take something?"

So the lad went and sat down, and before she asked him anything she set down wine before him and said, "Quicker is a drink than a tale." When he had taken that, he began and told her all that happened, and how he had seen her in his sleep, and when, and she was well pleased.

"And I saw thee in my sleep on the same night," said she.

He went away that day, and the old woman that he was lodging with asked him how he had got on, and he told her everything that had happened. And she went to the Bailie's daughter and told her all the good she could think of about the young lad. And after that he was often at the Bailie's house; and at last the daughter said she would marry him. "But I fear that will not do," said she. "Go home for a year, and when thou comest back I will contrive to marry thee," said she, "for it is the law of this country that no one must be married unless the Bailie himself gives her by the hand to her bridegroom," said she; and she left blessing with him.

Well, the lad went away as the girl said, and he was putting everything in order at home; and he told his father's brother all that had happened to him; but when the year was nearly out he set off for London again, and he had the second hundred with him and some good oatmeal cakes.

On the road whom should he meet but a Sassenach gentleman who was going the same road, and they began to talk. "Where art thou going?" said the Saxon. "Well, I am going to London," said he. "When I was there last I sowed some flax and I am going to see if it is as I left it. If it is well I will take it with me; if not, I will leave it."

"Well," said the other, "that is but a silly thing. How can flax seed be as thou has left it? It must be grown up and trodden down by ducks and geese, and eaten by hens long ago. I am going to London too; but I am going to marry the Bailie's daughter."

Well, they walked on together, and at long last the Saxon began to get hungry, and he had no food with him, and there was no house near; and he said to the other, "Wilt thou give me some of thy food?"

"Well," said the Gael, "I have but poor food—oaten bread; I will give you some if you will take it; but if I were a gentleman like you I would never travel without my own mother."

"How can I travel with my mother?" said the Saxon. "She is dead and buried long ago, and rotting in the earth; if not, why should I take her with me?"

And he took the oat cake and ate it, and they went on their way.

They had not gone far when a heavy shower came on, and the Gael had a rough plaid about him, but the Saxon had none, and he said to the other, "Wilt thou lend me thy plaid?"

"I will lend you a part of it," said the Gael; "but if I were a gentleman like you, I would never travel without my house, and I would not be indebted to anyone for favors."

"Thou art a fool," said the Saxon. "My house is four stories high. How could any man carry a house that is four stories high about with him?" But he wrapped the end of the Highlander's plaid about his shoulders, and they went on.

Well, they had not gone far till they came to a small river, and the water was deep after the rain, and there was no bridge, for in those days bridges were not so plentiful as they are now. The Saxon would not wet his feet, so he said to the Highlander, "Wilt thou carry me over?"

"Well," said the Gael, "I don't mind if I do; but if I were a gentleman like you, I would never travel without my own bridge, and I would not be in any man's debt for favors."

"Thou art a silly fellow," said the Saxon. "How can any man travel about with a bridge that is made of stone and lime and weighs as much as a house?"

But he got on the back of his fellow traveler nevertheless, and they traveled on till they got to London. Then the Saxon went to the house of the Bailie, and the other went to the little house of his countrywoman, who was the foster mother of the Bailie's daughter.

Well, the Saxon gentleman began to tell the Bailie all that had happened to him by the way; and he said, "I met with a Gael by the way, and he was a perfect fool—the greatest booby that man ever saw. He told me that he had sown flax here a year ago and that he was coming to fetch it, if he should find it as he left it, but that if he did not, he would leave it. And how should he find that after a year? He told me I should never travel without my mother, and my house, and my bridge; and how could a man travel with all these things? But though he was nothing but a fool, he was a good-natured fellow, for he gave me some of his food and lent me a bit of his plaid, and he carried me over a river."

"I know not but he was as wise as the man that was speaking to him," said the Bailie; for he was a wise man. "I'll tell you what he meant," said he. "He has left a girl in this town, and he is come to see if she is in the same mind as she was when he left her; if so, he will take her with him; if not, he will leave her; and he has sown flax. Your mother nourished you, and a gentleman like you should have his own nourishment with him. He meant that you should not be dependent on him. It was the booby that was with him. A gentleman like you should have his own shelter, and your house is your shelter when you are at home. A bridge is made for crossing a river, and a man should always be able to do that without help."

Said the Bailie, "The man was right, and he was no fool but a smart lad, and I should like to see him, and I would go to fetch him if I knew where he was."

Well, the next day the Bailie went to the house where the lad was, and he asked him to come home to his dinner. And the lad came, and he told the Bailie that he had understood all that had been said. "Now," said he, "as it is the law that no man may be married here unless the Bailie gives him the bride by the hand, will you be so kind as to give me the girl that I have come to marry, if she is in the same mind? I will have everything ready."

And the Bailie said, "I will do that, my smart lad, tomorrow, or whenever thou dost choose. I would go farther than that for such a smart boy."

"Well, I will be ready at such a house tomorrow," said the lad; and he went away to the foster mother's house.

When the morrow came, the Bailie's daughter disguised herself, and she went to the house of the foster mother, and the Gael had got a churchman there. And the Bailie came in, and he took his own daughter by the hand; but she would not give her hand to the lad. "Give thy hand, girl," said the Bailie. "It is an honor for thee to marry such a smart lad." And he gave her to him, and they were married according to law.

Then the Bailie went home, and he was to give his daughter by the hand to the Saxon gentleman that day; but the daughter was not to be found; and he was a widower, and she was keeping the house for him, and they could not find her anywhere.

"Well," said the Bailie, "I will lay a wager that Gael has got her, after all." And the Gael came in with the daughter, and he told them everything just as it had happened, from beginning to the end, and how he had plenty in his own country.

And the Bailie said, "Well, since I myself have given thee my daughter by the hand, it is a marriage, and I am glad that she has got a smart lad like thee for a husband."

And they made a wedding that lasted a year and a day, and they lived happily ever after; and if they have not died since then they are alive yet.

‌*≈§§*‌*≈§§*‌

17. The King of Love

ONCE UPON A TIME there was a man with three daughters who earned his living by gathering wild herbs. One day he took his youngest daughter with him. They came to a garden and began to gather vegetables. The daughter saw a fine radish and began to pull it up, when suddenly a Turk appeared and said, "Why have you opened my master's door? You must come in now, and he will decide on your punishment."

They went into the ground, more dead than alive; and when they were seated they saw a green bird come in and bathe in a pan of milk, then dry itself and become a handsome youth. He said to the Turk, "What do these persons want?" "Your worship, they pulled up a radish and opened the door of the cave." "How did we know," said the father, "that this was your excellency's house? My daughter saw a fine radish; it pleased her and she pulled it up." "Well, if that's the case," said the master, "your daughter shall stay here as my wife. Take this sack of gold and go; when you want to see your daughter, come and make yourself at home." The father took leave of his daughter and went away.

When the master was alone with her, he said, "You see, Rosella, you are now mistress here," and gave her all the keys. She was perfectly happy. One day while the green bird was away, her sisters took it into their heads to visit her, and asked her about her husband. Rosella said she did not know, for he had made her promise not to try to find out who he was. Her sisters, however, persuaded her, and when the bird returned and became a man, Rosella put on a downcast air. "What is the matter?" asked her husband. "Nothing." "You had better tell me." She let him question her awhile and at last said, "Well, then, if you want to know why I am out of sorts, it is because I wish to know your name."

Her husband told her that it would be the worse for her, but she insisted on knowing his name. So he made her put the gold basins on a chair and began to bathe his feet. "Rosella, do you really want to know my name?" "Yes." And the water came up to his waist, for he had become a bird and had got into the basin. Then he asked her the same question again, and again she answered yes, and the water was up to his mouth. "Rosella, do you really want to know my name?" "Yes, yes, yes!" Then know that I am called THE KING OF LOVE!" And saying this he disappeared, and the basins and the palace disappeared likewise, and Rosella found herself alone out in an open plain without a soul to help her. She called her servants, but no one answered her. Then she said, "Since my husband has disappeared, I must wander about alone and forlorn to seek him!"

The poor woman, who expected before long to become a mother, began her wanderings and at night arrived at another lonely plain. Then she felt her heart sink, and, not knowing what to do, she cried out:

> Ah! King of Love,
> You did it and said it.
> You disappeared from me in a golden basin,
> And who will shelter tonight
> This poor unfortunate one?

When she had uttered these words an ogress appeared and said, "Ah! wretch, how dare you go about seeking my nephew?" and was going to eat her up. But she took pity on her miserable state and gave her shelter for the night. The next morning she gave her a piece of bread and said, "We are seven sisters, all ogresses, and the worst of all is your mother-in-law. Look out for her!"

To be brief, the poor girl wandered about six days and met all six of the ogresses, who treated her in the same way. The seventh day, in great distress, she uttered her usual lament, and the sister of the King of Love appeared and said, "Rosella, while my mother is out, come up!" and she lowered the braids of her hair and pulled her up. Then she gave her something to eat and told her how to seize and pinch her mother until she cried out, "Let me alone for the sake of my son, the King of Love!"

Rosella did as she was told, but the ogress was so angry she was going to eat her. But her daughters threatened to abandon her if she did. "Well, then, I will write a letter, and Rosella must carry it to my friend." Poor Rosella was disheartened when she saw the letter, and, descending, found herself in the midst of a plain. She uttered her usual complaint, when the King of Love appeared and said, "You see your curiosity has brought you to this point!"

Poor thing! When she saw him she began to cry, and begged his pardon for what she had done. He took pity on her and said, "Now listen to what you must do. On your way you will come to a river of blood. You must bend down and take some up in your hands and say, 'How beautiful is this crystal water! Such water as this I have never drunk!' Then you will come to another stream of turbid water, and do the same there. Then you will find yourself in a garden where there is a great quantity of fruit. Pick some and eat it, saying, 'What fine pears! I have never eaten such pears as these.' Afterward you will come to an oven that bakes bread day and night, and no one buys any. When you have come there, say, 'Oh, what fine bread! Bread like this I have never eaten,' and eat some. Then you will come to an entrance guarded by two hungry dogs; give them a piece of bread to eat. Then you will come to a doorway all dirty and full of cobwebs; take a broom and sweep it clean. Halfway up the stairs you will find two giants, each with a dirty piece of meat by his side; take a brush and clean it for them. When you have entered the house, you will find a razor, a pair of scissors and a knife; take something and polish them. When you have done this, go and deliver your letter to my mother's friend. When she wants to make you enter, snatch up a little box on the table and run away. Take care to do all the things I have told you or else you will never escape alive."

Rosella did as she was told, and while the ogress was reading the letter Rosella seized the box and ran for her life. When the ogress had finished reading her letter, she called, "Rosella! Rosella!" When she received no answer, she perceived that she had been betrayed and cried out, "Razor, Scissors, Knife, cut her in pieces!" They answered, "As long as we have been razor, scissors and knife, when did you ever deign to polish us? Rosella came and brightened us up." The ogress, enraged, exclaimed, "Stairs, swallow her up!" "As long as I have been stairs, when did you ever deign to sweep me? Rosella came and swept me." The ogress cried in a passion, "Giants, crush her!" "As long as we have been giants, when did you ever deign to clean our food for us? Rosella came and did it."

Then the furious ogress called on the entrance to bury her

alive, the dogs to devour her, the furnace to burn her, the fruit tree to fall on her and the rivers to drown her, but they all remembered Rosella's kindness and refused to injure her.

Meanwhile Rosella continued her way, and at last became curious to know what was in the box she was carrying. So she opened it and a great quantity of little puppets came out. Some danced, some sang and some played on musical instruments. She amused herself some time with them, but when she was ready to go on, the little figures would not return to the box. Night approached, and she exclaimed, as she had so often before, "Ah! King of Love," and the rest of her plaint.

Then her husband appeared and said, "Oh! your curiosity will be the death of you!" and commanded the puppets to enter the box again. Then Rosella went her way and arrived safely at her mother-in-law's. When the ogress saw her she exclaimed, "You owe this luck to my son, the King of Love!" and was going to devour poor Rosella, but her daughters said, "Poor child! she has brought you the box; why do you want to eat her?" "Well and good. You want to marry my son, the King of Love. Then take these six mattresses and go and fill them with bird's feathers!"

Rosella descended and began to wander about, uttering her usual lament. When her husband appeared, Rosella told him what had happened. He whistled and the King of the Birds appeared and commanded all the birds to come and drop their feathers, fill the six beds and carry them back to the ogress, who again said that her son had helped Rosella. However, she went and made up her son's bed with the six mattresses, and that very day she made him marry the daughter of the King of Portugal. Then she called Rosella, and, telling her that her son was married, bade her kneel before the nuptial bed, holding two lighted torches. Rosella obeyed, but soon the King of Love, under the plea that Rosella was not in condition to hold the torches any longer, persuaded his bride to change places with her. Just as the queen took the torches in her hands, the earth opened and swallowed her up, and the king remained happy with Rosella.

When the ogress heard what had happened, she clasped her hands over her head and declared that Rosella's child should not be born until she unclasped her hands. Then the King of Love had a catafalque erected and stretched himself on it as though he were dead, and had all the bells tolled and made the people cry, "How did the King of Love die?" The ogress heard it and asked, "What is that noise?"

Her daughters told her that their brother was dead from her fault. When the ogress heard this, she unclasped her hands, saying, "How did my son die?" At that moment Rosella's child was born. When the ogress heard it, she burst a blood vessel and died. Then the King of Love took his wife and sisters, and they remained happy and contented.

❧❦❧❦❧

18. The Small-Tooth Dog

ONCE UPON A TIME there was a merchant who traveled about the world a great deal. On one of his journeys thieves attacked him, and they would have taken both his life and his money if a large dog had not come to his rescue and driven the thieves away. When the dog had driven the thieves away, he took the merchant to his house, which was a very handsome one, and he dressed his wounds and nursed him until he was well.

As soon as he was able to travel, the merchant began his journey home, but before starting he told the dog how grateful he was for his kindness and asked him what reward he could offer in return, and he said he would not refuse to give him the most precious thing that he had.

And so the merchant said to the dog, "Will you accept a fish that I have that can speak twelve languages?"

"No," said the dog, "I will not."

"Or a goose that lays golden eggs?"

"No," said the dog, "I will not."

"Or a mirror in which you can see what anybody is thinking about?"

"No," said the dog, "I will not."

"Then what will you have?" said the merchant.

"I will have none of such presents," said the dog, "but let me fetch your daughter and take her to my house."

When the merchant heard this he was grieved, but what he had promised had to be done. So he said to the dog, "You can come and fetch my daughter after I have been at home for a week."

So at the end of the week the dog came to the merchant's house to fetch his daughter, but when he got there he stayed outside the door and would not go in. The merchant's daughter did as her father told her and came out of the house dressed for a journey and ready to go with the dog. When the dog saw her, he looked pleased and said, "Jump on my back and I will take you away to my house." So she mounted on the dog's back, and away they went at a great pace until they reached the dog's house, which was many miles off.

But after she had been a month at the dog's house, she began to mope and cry.

"What are you crying for?" asked the dog.

"Because I want to go back to my father," she answered.

"If you will promise me," the dog said, "that you will not stay at home more than three days, I will take you there. But first of all, what do you call me?"

"A great, foul, small-tooth dog," said she.

"Then," said he, "I will not let you go."

But she cried so pitifully that he promised again to take her home. "But before we start," said he, "tell me what you call me."

"Oh," she said, "your name is Sweet-as-a-Honeycomb."

"Jump on my back," said he, "and I'll take you home."

So he trotted away with her on his back for forty miles, when they came to a stile. "And what do you call me?" asked he, before they got over the stile.

Thinking that she was safe on her way, the girl said, "A great, foul, small-tooth dog."

But when she said this, he did not jump over the stile but turned right round about at once and galloped back to his own house with the girl on his back.

Another week went by and again the girl wept so bitterly that the dog promised her again to take her to her father's house.

So the girl got on the dog's back again, and they reached the first stile as before. There the dog stopped and said, "And what do you call me?"

"Sweet-as-a-Honeycomb," she replied.

So the dog leaped over the stile, and they went on for twenty miles until they came to another stile. "And what do you call me?" said the dog, with a wag of his tail.

As she was thinking more of her father and her own home than of the dog, she answered, "A great, foul, small-tooth dog."

Then the dog was in a great rage, and he turned right round about and galloped back to his own house as before.

After she had cried for another week, the dog promised again to take her back to her father's house. So she mounted upon his back once more, and when they got to the first stile the dog said, "And what do you call me?"

"Sweet-as-a-Honeycomb," she said.

So the dog jumped over the stile and away they went, for now the girl made up her mind to say the most loving things she could think of—until they reached her father's house.

When they got to the door of the merchant's house, the dog said, "And what do you call me?"

Just at that moment the girl forgot the loving things that she meant to say and began, "A great—" but the dog began to turn and she got fast hold of the door latch and was going to say "foul," when she saw how grieved the dog looked and remembered how good and patient he had been with her, so she said, "Sweeter-than-a-Honeycomb."

When she had said this, she thought the dog would have been content and have galloped away. But instead of that he suddenly stood up on his hind legs, and with his forelegs he pulled off his dog's head and tossed it high in the air. His hairy coat dropped off, and there stood the handsomest young man in the world, with the finest and smallest teeth you ever saw.

Of course, they were married, and lived together happily.

～ॐ～ॐ～

19. *The Horse-Devil and the Witch*

THERE WAS once upon a time a padishah (emperor) who had three daughters. One day the old father made him ready for a journey, and, calling to him his three daughters, straightly charged them to feed and water his favorite horse, even though they neglected everything else. He loved the horse so much that he would not suffer any stranger to come near it.

So the padishah went on his way, but when the eldest daughter brought the fodder into the stable, the horse would not let her come near him. Then the middling daughter brought the forage, and he treated her likewise. Last of all the youngest daughter brought the forage, and when the horse saw her he never budged an inch but let her feed him and then return to her sisters. The two elder sisters were content that the youngest should take care of the horse, so they troubled themselves about it no more.

The padishah came home, and the first thing he asked was whether they had provided the horse with everything. "He wouldn't let us come near him," said the two elder sisters. "It was our youngest sister here who took care of him."

No sooner had the padishah heard this than he gave his

youngest daughter to the horse to wife, but his two other daughters he gave to the sons of his chief mufti and his grand vizier, and they celebrated the three marriages at a great banquet which lasted forty days. Then the youngest daughter turned into the stable, but the two eldest dwelt in a splendid palace. In the daytime the youngest sister had only a horse for a husband and a stable for a dwelling; but in the nighttime the stable became a garden of roses, the horse-husband a handsome hero, and they lived in a world of their own. Nobody knew of it but the two of them. They passed the day together as best they could, but eventide was the time of their impatient desires.

One day the padishah held a tournament at the palace. Many gallant warriors entered the lists, but none strove so valiantly as the husbands of the sultan's elder daughters.

"Only look now!" said the two elder daughters to their sister who dwelt in the stable. "Only look now! how our husbands overthrow all the other warriors with their lances. Our two lords are not so much lords as lions! Where is this horse-husband of thine, prithee?"

On hearing this from his wife, the horse-husband shivered all over, turned into a man, threw himself on horseback, told his wife not to betray him on any account, and in an instant appeared within the lists. He overthrew every one with his lance, unhorsed his two brothers-in-law and reappeared in the stable again as if he had never left it.

The next day when the sports began again, the two elder sisters mocked as before, but then the unknown hero appeared again, conquered and vanished. On the third day the horse-husband said to his wife, "If ever I should come to grief or thou shouldst need my help, take these three wisps of hair, burn them, and it will help thee wherever thou art." With that he hastened to the games again and triumphed over his brothers-in-law. Everyone was amazed at his skill, the two sisters likewise, and again they said to their younger sister, "Look how these heroes excel in prowess! They are very different from thy dirty horse-husband!"

The girl could not endure standing there with nothing to say for herself, so she told her sisters that the handsome hero was no other than her horse-husband—and no sooner had she pointed at him than he vanished from before them as if he had never been. Then only did she call to mind her lord's command to her not to betray his secret, and away she hurried to the stable. But 'twas all in vain. Neither horse nor man came to her, and at midnight there was neither rose nor rose garden.

"Alas!" wept the girl, "I have betrayed my lord; I have broken my word—what a crime is mine!" She never closed an eye all that night, but wept till morning. When the red dawn appeared, she went to her father, the padishah, complained to him that she had lost her horse-husband and begged that she might go to the ends of the earth to seek him. In vain her father tried to keep her back; in vain he pointed out to her that her husband was now most probably among devils and she would never be able to find him. Turn her from her resolution he could not. What could he do but let her go on her way?

With a great desire the damsel set out on her quest. She went on and on till her tender body was all aweary, and at last she sank down exhausted at the foot of a great mountain. Then she called to mind the three hairs, and she took out one and set fire to it. And lo! her lord and master was in her arms again, and they could not speak for joy.

"Did I not bid thee tell none of my secret?" cried the youth sorrowfully. "And now if my hag of a mother sees thee she will instantly tear thee to pieces. This mountain is our dwelling place. She will be here immediately, and woe to thee if she sees thee!"

The poor sultan's daughter was terribly frightened and wept worse than ever at the thought of losing her lord again, after all the trouble in finding him. The heart of the devil's son was touched at her sorrow. He struck her once, changed her into an apple and put her on the shelf. The hag flew down from the mountain with a terrible racket and screeched out that she smelt the smell of man, and her mouth watered for the taste of human flesh. In vain her son denied that there was any human flesh there. She would not believe him one bit.

"If thou wilt swear by the egg not to be offended, I'll show thee what I've hidden," said her son. The hag swore, and her son gave the apple a tap, and there before them stood the beautiful damsel. "Behold my wife!" said he to his mother. The old mother said never a word; what was done could not be undone. "I'll give the bride something to do all the same," thought she.

They lived a couple of days together in peace and quiet, but the hag was only waiting for her son to leave the house. At last one day the youth had work to do elsewhere, and scarcely had he put his foot out of door when the hag said to the damsel, "Come sweep and sweep not!" And with that she went out and said she should not be back till evening. The girl thought to herself again and again, "What am I to do now? What did she mean by 'sweep and sweep not'?" Then she thought of the hairs, and she took out and burned the second hair also. Immediately her lord stood before her and asked her what was the matter, and the girl told him of his mother's command, "Sweep and sweep not!" Then her lord explained to her that she was to sweep out the chamber but not to sweep the antechamber.

The girl did as she was told, and when the hag came home in the evening she asked the girl whether she had accomplished her task. "Yes, little mother," replied the bride. "I have swept and I have not swept." "Thou daughter of a dog," cried the old witch, "not thine own wit but my son's mouth hath told you this thing."

The next morning when the hag got up, she gave the damsel vases and told her to fill them with tears. The moment the hag had gone, the damsel placed the three vases before her and wept and wept, but what could her few teardrops do to fill them? Then she took out and burned the third hair.

Again her lord appeared before her and explained to her that she must fill the three vases with water and then put a pinch of salt in each vase. The girl did so, and when the hag came home in the evening and demanded an account of her work, the girl showed her the three vases full of tears. "Thou daughter of a dog!" chided the old woman again. "That is not thy work; but I'll do for thee yet, and for my son too."

The next day she devised some other task for her to do. But her son guessed that his mother would vex the wench, so he hastened home to his bride. There the poor thing was worrying herself about it all alone, for the third hair was now burnt and she did not know how to set about doing the task laid upon her. "Well, there is now nothing for it but to run away," said her lord, "for she won't rest now till she hath done thee a mischief." And with that he took his wife, and out into the wide world they went.

In the evening the hag came home and saw neither her son nor his bride. "They have flown, the dogs!" cried the hag, with a threatening voice, and she called to her sister, who was also a witch, to make ready and go in pursuit of her son and his bride. So the witch jumped into a pitcher, snatched up a serpent for a whip and went after them.

The demon-lover saw his aunt coming and in an instant changed the girl into a bathing house and himself into a bathman sitting down at the gate. The witch leaped from the pitcher, went to the bathkeeper and asked him if he had not seen a young boy and girl pass by that way.

"I have only just warmed up my bath," said the youth. "There's nobody inside it. If thou dost not believe me, thou canst go and look for thyself." The witch thought, " 'Tis impossible to get a sensible word out of a fellow of this sort," so she jumped into her pitcher, flew back and told her sister that she couldn't find them. The other hag asked her whether she had exchanged words with anyone on the road. "Yes," replied the younger sister. "There was a bathhouse by the roadside, and I asked the owner of it about them; but he was either a fool or deaf, so I took no notice of him."

" 'Tis thou who wert the fool," snarled her elder sister. "Didst thou not recognize in him my son, and in the bathhouse my daughter-in-law?" Then she called her second sister and sent her after the fugitives.

The devil's son saw his second aunt flying along in her pitcher. Then he gave his wife a tap and turned her into a spring, but he himself sat down beside it and began to draw water out of it with a pitcher. The witch went up to him and asked him whether he had seen a girl and a boy pass by that way.

"There's drinkable water in this spring," replied he, with a vacant stare. "I am always drawing it." The witch thought she had to do with a fool, turned back and told her sister that she had not met with them. Her sister asked her if she had not come across anyone by the way. "Yes indeed," replied she. "A half-witted fellow was drawing water from a spring, but I couldn't get a single sensible word out of him."

"That half-witted fellow was my son, the spring was his wife, and a pretty wiseacre thou art," screeched her sister. "I shall have to go myself, I see." And with that she jumped into her pitcher, snatched up a serpent to serve her as a whip, and off she went.

Meanwhile the youth looked back again and saw his mother coming after them. He gave the girl a tap and changed her into a tree, but he himself turned into a serpent and coiled himself round the tree. The witch recognized them and drew near to the tree to break it to pieces, but when she saw the serpent coiled round it she was afraid she would kill her own son in destroying the tree. So she said, "Son, son! show me at least the girl's little finger, and then I'll leave you both in peace."

The son saw that he could not free himself from her any other way, and that she must have at least a little morsel of the damsel to nibble at. So he showed her one of the girl's little fingers, and the old hag wrenched it off and returned to her domains with it. Then the youth gave the girl a tap and himself another tap, put on human shape again, and away they went to the girl's father, the padishah. The youth, because the term of the evil spell which had been upon him had now expired, remained a mortal man, and the diabolical part of him stayed at home with his witch mother and her kindred. The padishah rejoiced greatly in his children, gave them a wedding banquet with a wave of his finger, and they inherited the realm after his death.

⋙⋘⋙⋘

20. The Dead Lover

MANY, MANY YEARS since, there lived in the kingdom of Olmilsong two brothers, and they were both married. Now the elder brother and his wife were niggardly and envious, while the younger brother was of quite a different disposition.

Once upon a time the elder brother, who had contrived to gather together abundance of riches, gave a great feast and invited many people to partake of it. When this was known, the younger thought to himself, "Although my elder brother has hitherto not treated me very well, yet he will now, no doubt, since he has invited so many people to his feast, invite also me and my wife." This he certainly expected, but yet he was not invited. "Probably," thought he, "my brother will summon me tomorrow morning to the brandy drinking." Because, however, he was not even invited unto that, he grieved very sore and said to himself, "This night when my brother's wife has drunk the brandy, I will go unto the house and steal somewhat."

When, however, he had glided into the treasure chamber of his brother, there lay the wife of his brother near her husband. But presently she arose and went into the kitchen and cooked meat and sweet food, and went out of the door with it. The concealed one did not venture at this moment to steal anything, but said to himself, "Before I steal anything, I will just see what all this means."

So saying, he went forth and followed the woman to a mountain where the dead were wont to be laid. On the top, upon a green mound, lay a beautiful ornamental tomb over the body of a dead man. This man had formerly been the lover of the woman. Even when afar off she called unto the dead man by name, and when she had come unto him she threw her arms about his neck. And the younger brother was nigh unto her and saw all that she did.

The woman next handed the sweet food which she had prepared to the dead man, and because the teeth of the corse did not open, she separated them with a pair of brazen pincers and pushed the food into his mouth. Suddenly the pincers bounced back from the teeth of the dead man and snapped off the tip of the woman's nose; while at the same time the teeth of the dead man closed together and bit off the end of the woman's tongue. Upon this the woman took up the dish with the food and went back to her home.

The younger brother thereupon followed her home and concealed himself in the treasure chamber, and the wife laid herself down again by her husband. Presently the man began to move, when the wife immediately cried out, "Woe is me! woe is me! was there ever such a man?" And the man said, "What is the matter now?" The wife replied, "The point of my tongue and the tip of my nose, both these thou hast bitten off. What can a woman do without these two things? Tomorrow the chan shall be made acquainted with this conduct." Thus spake she, and the younger brother fled from the treasure chamber without stealing anything.

On the following morning the woman presented herself before the chan and addressed him, saying, "My husband has this night treated me shamefully. Whatsoever punishment may be awarded to him, I myself will see it inflicted."

But the husband persisted in asserting, "Of all this I know nothing!" Because the complaint of the wife seemed well-founded, and the man could not exculpate himself, the chan said, "Because of his evil deeds, let this man be burnt."

When the younger brother heard what had befallen the elder, he went to see him. And after the younger one had related to him all the affair, he betook himself unto the chan, saying, "That the evildoer may be really discovered, let both the woman and her husband be summoned before you. I will clear up the mystery."

When they were both present, the younger brother related the wife's visit to the dead man, and because the chan would not give credence unto his story, he said, "In the mouth of the dead man you will find the end of the woman's tongue; and the bloody tip of her nose you will find in the pincers of brass. Send thither and see if it be not so."

Thus spake he, and people were sent to the place, and they confirmed all that he had asserted. Upon this the chan said, "Since the matter stands thus, let the woman be placed upon a pile of fagots and consumed with fire." And the woman was placed upon the pile of fagots and consumed with fire.

త్రిక్రిస్‌

21. The Sneezing Bride

BILLY MAC DANIEL was once as likely a young man as ever shook his brogue at a patron, emptied a quart or handled a shillelagh; fearing for nothing but the want of drink, caring for nothing but who should pay for it, and thinking of nothing but how to make fun over it. Drunk or sober, a word and a blow was ever the way with Billy Mac Daniel; and a mighty easy way it is of either getting into or of ending a dispute. More is the pity that through the means of his thinking and fearing and caring for nothing, this same Billy Mac Daniel fell into bad company, for surely the good people are the worst of all company anyone could come across.

It so happened that Billy was going home one clear frosty night not long after Christmas. The moon was round and bright, but although it was as fine a night as heart could wish for, he felt pinched with the cold. "By my word," chattered Billy, "a drop of good liquor would be no bad thing to keep a man's soul from freezing in him, and I wish I had a full measure of the best."

"Never wish it twice, Billy," said a little man in a three-cornered hat, bound all about with gold lace, and with great silver buckles in his shoes, so big that it was a wonder how he could carry them. And he held out a glass as big as himself, filled with as good liquor as ever eye looked on or lip tasted.

"Success, my little fellow," said Billy Mac Daniel, nothing

daunted, though well he knew the little man to belong to the good people. "Here's your health, anyway, and thank you kindly, no matter who pays for the drink." And he took the glass and drained it to the very bottom without ever taking a second breath to it.

"Success," said the little man, "and you're heartily welcome, Billy, but don't think to cheat me as you have done others. Out with your purse and pay me like a gentleman."

"Is it I pay you?" said Billy. "Could I not just take you up and put you in my pocket as easily as a blackberry?"

"Billy Mac Daniel," said the little man, getting very angry, "you shall be my servant for seven years and a day, and that is the way I will be paid. So make ready to follow me."

When Billy heard this, he began to be very sorry for having used such bold words towards the little man. And he felt himself, yet could not tell how, obliged to follow the little man the livelong night about the country, up and down and over hedge and ditch, and through bog and brake without any rest.

When morning began to dawn, the little man turned round to him and said, "You may now go home, Billy, but on your peril don't fail to meet me in the Fort field tonight; or if you do, it may be the worse for you in the long run. If I find you a good servant, you will find me an indulgent master."

Home went Billy Mac Daniel, and though he was tired and weary enough, never a wink of sleep could he get for thinking of the little man. But he was afraid not to do his bidding, so up he got in the evening and away he went to the Fort field. He was not long there before the little man came towards him and said, "Billy, I want to go a long journey to-night, so saddle one of my horses, and you may saddle another for yourself, as you are to go along with me and may be tired after your walk last night."

Billy thought this very considerate of his master and thanked him accordingly. "But," said he, "if I may be so bold, sir, I would ask which is the way to your stable, for never a thing do I see but the Fort here, and the old thorn tree in the corner of the field, and the stream running at the bottom of the hill, with the bit of bog over against us."

"Ask no questions, Billy," said the little man, "but go over to that bit of bog and bring me two of the stoutest rushes you can find."

Billy did accordingly, wondering what the little man would be at. And he picked out two of the stoutest rushes he could find, with a little bunch of brown blossom stuck at the side of each, and brought them to his master.

"Get up, Billy," said the little man, taking one of the rushes from him and striding across it.

"Where shall I get up, please your honor?" said Billy.

"Why, upon horseback, like me, to be sure," said the little man.

"Is it after making a fool of me you'd be," said Billy, "bidding me get a-horseback upon that bit of a rush? Maybe you want to persuade me that the rush I pulled but while ago out of the bog over there is a horse."

"Up! up! and no words," said the little man, looking very angry. "The best horse you ever rode was but a fool to it." So Billy, thinking all this was a joke and fearing to vex his master, straddled across the rush.

"Borram! Borram! Borram!" cried the little man three times (which in English means "become great"), and Billy did the same after him. Presently the rushes swelled up into fine horses, and away they went full speed. But Billy, who had put the rush between his legs without much minding how he did it, found himself sitting on horseback the wrong way, which was rather awkward, with his face to the horse's tail. So quickly had his steed started off with him that he had no power to turn around, and there was therefore nothing for it but to hold on by the tail.

At last they came to their journey's end and stopped at the gate of a fine house. "Now, Billy," said the little man, "do as you see me do and follow me close. But as you did not know your horse's head from his tail, mind that your own head does not spin round until you can't tell whether you are standing on it or on your heels, for remember that old liquor, though able to make a cat speak, can make a man dumb."

The little man then said some queer kind of words out of which Billy could make no meaning, but he contrived to say them after him for all that, and in they both went through the keyhole of the door, and through one keyhole after another until they got into the wine cellar, which was well stored with all kinds of wine.

The little man fell to drinking as hard as he could, and Billy, nowise disliking the example, did the same. "The best of masters are you, surely," said Billy to him, "no matter who is the next. And well pleased will I be with your service if you continue to give me plenty of drink."

"I have made no bargain with you," said the little man, "and will make none. But up and follow me." Away they went, through keyhole after keyhole. And each, mounting upon the rush which he left at the hall door, scampered off, kicking the clouds before them like snowballs as soon as the words "Borram, Borram, Borram" had passed their lips.

When they came back to the Fort field, the little man dismissed Billy, bidding him to be there the next night at the same hour. Thus did they go on, night after night, shaping their course one night here and another night there—sometimes north and sometimes east, and sometimes south, until there was not a gentleman's wine cellar in all Ireland they had not visited, and could tell the flavor of every wine in it as well —ay, better—than the butler himself.

One night when Billy Mac Daniel met the little man as usual in the Fort field and was going to the bog to fetch the horses for their journey, his master said to him, "Billy, I shall want another horse tonight, for perhaps we may bring back more company with us than we take." So Billy, who now knew better than to question any order given to him by his master, brought a third rush, much wondering who it might be that would travel back in their company, and whether he was about to have a fellow servant. "If I have," thought Billy, "he shall go forth and fetch the horses from the bog every night, for I don't see why I am not, every inch of me, as good a gentleman as my master."

Well, away they went, Billy leading the third horse, and never stopped until they came to a snug farmer's house in the county Limerick, close under the old castle of Carrigogunniel, that was built, they say, by the great Brian Boru. Within the house there was great carousing going forward, and the little man stopped outside for some time to listen. Then turning around all of a sudden, he said, "Billy, I will be a thousand years old tomorrow!"

"God bless us, sir," said Billy, "will you?"

"Don't say these words again, Billy," said the little man, "or you will be my ruin forever. Now Billy, as I will be a thousand years in the world tomorrow, I think it is full time for me to get married."

"I think so too, without any kind of doubt at all," said Billy, "if ever you mean to marry."

"And to that purpose," said the little man, "have I come all the way to Carrigogunniel, for in this house this very night is young Darby Riley going to be married to Bridget Rooney. And as she is a tall and comely girl and has come of decent people, I think of marrying her myself and taking her off with me."

"And what will Darby Riley say to that?" asked Billy.

"Silence!" said the little man, putting on a mighty severe look. "I did not bring you here with me to ask questions." And without holding further argument, he began saying the queer words which had the power of passing him through the keyhole as free as air, and which Billy thought himself mighty clever to be able to say after him.

In they both went, and for the better viewing of the company the little man perched himself up as nimbly as a cock sparrow upon one of the big beams which went across the house over all their heads. Billy did the same upon another facing him, but not being much accustomed to roosting in such a place, his legs hung down as untidy as may be, and it was quite clear he had not taken pattern after the way in which the little man had bundled himself up together. If the latter had been a tailor all his life, he could not have sat more contentedly upon his haunches.

There they were looking down upon the fun that was going forward. And under them were the priest and piper and father of Darby Riley, with Darby's two brothers and his uncle's son. Also the father and mother of Bridget Rooney, and proud enough the old couple were that night of their daughter—as good right they had—and her four sisters with brand-new ribbons on their caps, and her three brothers all looking as clean and as clever as any three boys in Munster. And there were uncles and aunts and gossips and cousins enough besides to make a full house of it—and plenty there was to eat and drink on the table for every one of them, if they had been double the number.

Now it happened just as Mrs. Rooney had helped his reverence to the first cut of the pig's head which was placed before her, beautifully bolstered up with white savoy cabbages, that the bride gave a sneeze which made everyone at table start, but not a soul said "God bless us." All thinking that the priest would have done so, as he ought if he had done his duty, no one wished to take the word out of his mouth, which unfortunately was preoccupied with pig's head and greens. And after a moment's pause the fun and merriment of the bridal feast went on without the pious benediction.

Of this circumstance both Billy and his master were no inattentive spectators from their exalted stations. "Ha!" exclaimed the little man, throwing one leg from under him with a joyous flourish, and his eye twinkled with a strange light, whilst his eyebrows became elevated into the curvature of Gothic arches—"Ha!" said he, leering down at the bride and then up at Billy. "I have half of her now, surely. Let her sneeze but twice more and she is mine in spite of priest, massbook and Darby Riley."

Again the fair Bridget sneezed, but it was so gently and she blushed so much that few except the little man took, or seemed to take, any notice. No one thought of saying "God bless us."

Billy all this time regarded the poor girl with a most rueful expression of countenance, for he could not help thinking what a terrible thing it was for a nice young girl of nineteen, with large blue eyes, transparent skin and dimpled cheeks, suffused with health and joy, to be obliged to marry an ugly bit of a man who was a thousand years old, barring a day.

At this critical moment the bride gave a third sneeze, and Billy roared out with all his might, "God save us!" Whether this exclamation resulted from what he had just been thinking or from mere force of habit he never could tell exactly himself, but no sooner was it uttered than the little man, his face glowing with rage and disappointment, sprang from the beam on which he had perched himself, and shrieking out in the shrill voice of a cracked bagpipe, "I discharge you from my service, Billy Mac Daniel—take that for your wages," gave poor Billy a most furious kick in the back, which sent the unfortunate servant sprawling upon his face and hands right in the middle of the supper table.

If Billy was astonished, how much more so was every one of the company into which he was thrown with so little ceremony. But when they heard his story, Father Cooney laid down his fork and knife and married Bridget to Darby out of hand with all speed. And Billy Mac Daniel danced the rinka at their wedding, and plenty did he drink at it too, which was what he thought more of than dancing.

❧❧❧

22. *Donagha Dee and His Wife*

THERE WAS once a long time ago a poor man whose name was Donagha Dee, and he lived in a small cabin not far from a forest in the heart of the County Kerry. Ireland at that time was not so bare as it is now but was covered with great forests; inasmuch that, it is said, a squirrel might have traveled from Dingle-de-Conch to the city of Cork without once touching the ground. Now, you must know, Donagha Dee was a very poor man and had a scolding wife; so that, between his wife and his poverty, he could scarcely ever get a moment's peace. A man might perhaps put up with a cross word now and then from a woman if she was pretty, or had any other good about her. But unluckily Donagha's wife had nothing at all to recommend her; for besides being cross she was as old and ugly as the black gentleman himself; so you may well suppose they had but a dog-and-cattish sort of life.

One morning in the beautiful month of May, Donagha was quietly smoking his dudeen (pipe) in the chimney corner when his wife, coming in from the well with a can of water, opened upon him all at once, as if there were a thousand beagles in her throat. "You lazy, good-for-nothing stocagh!" said she. "Have you nothing else to do this blessed morning but to sit poking over the ashes with your dudeen stuck in your jaw? Wouldn't it be fitter for you to be gathering a brosna (firewood) than be sitting there as if you were fastened to the bench with a twelvepenny nail?"

All this she said, and much more; to which Donagha made no reply but quietly took his billhook and gad, and away with him to the forest. I don't know what made him so quiet with her; maybe he wasn't in fighting humor, and maybe he thought it best to get out of her way, for they say a good retreat is better than a bad fight any day.

A beautiful fine day it was, sure enough. The sun was dancing through the trees, and the little birds were singing like so many pipers at a pattern, so that it was like a new life to Donagha, who, feeling the cockles of his heart rise within him, took up his billhook and began to work as contented as if he had nothing at home to fret him. But he wasn't long at work when he was amazed at the sound of a voice that seemed to come out of the middle of the wood; and though it was the sweetest voice he had ever heard, he couldn't help being frightened at it too, a little, for there was something in it that wasn't like the voice of man, woman or child.

"Donagha! Donagha!" said the voice. But Donagha didn't much like to answer. "Donagha!" said the voice again. He thought maybe it would be better for him to speak. "Here I am," says he; and then the voice answered back again. "Donagha, don't be frightened," said the voice, "for sure I'm only St. Brandon that's sent to tell you, because you're a good Christian and minds your duty, you shall have two wishes granted to you, so take care what you wish for, Donagha."

"Och, success to you for one saint, anyhow," said Donagha, as he began to work again, thinking all the time what in the wide world he had best wish for. Would he take riches for his first wish? Then what should he take for the second? A good wife—or wouldn't it be better not to have any wife at all? Well, he thought for a long time without being able to make up his mind what to wish for.

Night was coming on, and so Donagha, gathering a great bundle of firewood up, tied it well with his gad, and heaving it upon his shoulder, away home with him. Donagha was fairly spent with the work of the day so that it was no wonder he should find the load on his shoulder rather too much for him, and stumbling with weariness, he was obliged at length to throw it down. Sitting upon his bundle, 'twas Donagha was in great botheration. The night was closing in fast, and he knew not what kind of a welcome he'd have before him if he either stayed out too late or returned without a full load of firing.

"Would to heaven," says he in his distress and forgetting the power of his wish, "would to heaven this brosna would carry me instead of my being obliged to carry it!"

Immediately the brosna began to move on with him, and seated on top of it poor Donagha cut a mighty odd figure surely; for until he reached his own door he never stopped roaring out a thousand murders, he was so vexed with himself at having thrown away one of his wishes so foolishly.

His wife Vauria (Mary) was standing at the door looking out for him, ready to give him a good saletting; but she was fairly struck dumb at seeing Donagha so queerly mounted, and at hearing him cry out in such a manner. When she came a little to herself, she asked Donagha a thousand questions about how he came to be riding upon a brosna; and poor Donagha, being so questioned, could not help telling her the whole story just as it happened.

It was then that she was mad angry in earnest with him, to think that he would throw away his luck. Donagha, worn out and perplexed, was not able to bear it, and at length cried out as loud as he could, "I wish to heaven, I wish to heaven, you old scold that's the plague of my life—I wish to heaven that Ireland was between us!"

No sooner said than done, for he was whipped up by a whirlwind and dropped at the northeastern side of Ireland, where Donaghadee now stands, and Vauria, house and all, was carried off at the same time to its most southwestern spot, beyond Dingle, and not far from the great Atlantic Ocean. The place, to this day, is known by the name of Tig-na-Vauria, or Mary's house; and when the people would speak of places wide asunder, it has become a sort of proverb to say, as far as Tig-na-Vauria from Donaghadee!

❧❧

23. *The Specter Bridegroom*

FRANK LENINE, only son of a well-to-do farmer of Boscean, fell deeply in love with his mother's maidservant, Nancy Trenoweth, as pretty as a primrose but with very little education. Her mother was a kind of white witch and her family in poor circumstances. As Frank's parents had always given him everything he wanted, he thought they would not stand in the way of his marrying Nancy. However, they did, his father feeling it would be a degradation for a Lenine to marry a Trenoweth. Old Lenine sent Nancy home to her parents in Alsia Mill and sternly forbade Frank ever to see her again.

To keep lovers apart, however, much more is necessary than a parent's command, and especially lovers as impatient of restraint as Frank and Nancy. Rarely an evening passed that did not find them together in some retired nook. The Holy Well was a favorite meeting place, and here the most solemn vows were made. Locks of hair were exchanged; a wedding ring, taken from the finger of a corpse, was broken when they vowed that they would be united either dead or alive. And they even climbed the granite pile at Treryn at night and repeated by the Logan Rock the same strong vow.

Time passed onward thus unhappily, and as a result of the endeavors to quench out the passion by force, it grew stronger, and, like imprisoned steam, eventually burst through all restraint. Nancy's parents discovered at length that the moonlight meetings between the two impulsive youths had a natural result, and they now doubled their efforts to compel Frank to marry their daughter.

Old Lenine could not be brought to consent to this, and he firmly resolved to remove his son entirely from what he considered the bad influence of the Trenoweths. He decided to go to Plymouth, to take his son with him, and if possible, to send him away to sea, hoping thus to wean him from his folly, as he considered this love-madness. Frank, poor fellow, with the best intentions, was not capable of any sustained resistance, and consequently at length succumbed to his father, and to escape his importunity, he entered a ship bound for India and bade adieu to his native land.

This happened in days when letters could be forwarded only with extreme difficulty. Besides, Frank did not know how to write. Consequently, Nancy never heard from her lover. A baby was born into a troublesome world. The infant was a real solace to the young mother, and became a special favorite with its grandmother. Nancy was subdued in spirit, but her affliction had given force to her character, and she had been heard to declare that wherever Frank might be, she was ever present with him; whatever might be the temptations of the hour, that her influence was all-powerful over him for good. She felt that no distance could separate their souls; that no time could be long enough to destroy the bond between them.

A period of distress now fell upon the Trenoweths, and it was necessary that Nancy should leave her home once more and go again into service. She found a situation in the village of Kimyall in the parish of Paul, and her mother took charge of the babe. Winter was coming on, and nearly three years had passed since Frank left his country. No one, not even his parents, had received a word from him. His parents now desired to take Nancy's child, but the Trenoweths would not part with it. The Lenines went so far even as to try to persuade Nancy to live with them again. However, she was not at all disposed to submit to their wishes.

On Allhallows Eve two farm girls who had become Nancy's friends persuaded her—no difficult task—to go with them and sow the hemp seed. The three maidens stole out unperceived into Kimyall town place at midnight to perform their incantation. Nancy was the first to sow, the others being less bold than she. Intrepidly she advanced, saying, as she scattered the seed:

> "Hemp seed I sow thee,
> Hemp seed grow thee,
> And he who will my true love be,
> Come after me
> And shaw thee."

This was repeated three times, when, looking back over her left shoulder, she saw Frank. But he looked so angry that she shrieked with fear and broke the spell. One of the other girls, notwithstanding, resolved now to make trial of the spell. The result of her labors was the vision of a white coffin. Fear now fell on all, and they went home sorrowful, to spend each one a sleepless night.

December came with its storms, and during one terrific night a large vessel was thrown upon the rocks in Bernowhall Cliff, and beaten by the impetuous waves, she was soon in pieces. Amongst the bodies of the crew washed ashore, nearly all of whom had perished, was Frank Lenine. He was not dead when found, but the only words he lived to speak were begging the people to send for Nancy Trenoweth that he might make her his wife before he died.

Rapidly sinking, Frank was borne by his friends on a litter to Boscean, but he died as he reached the town place. His parents, overwhelmed in their own sorrows, thought nothing of Nancy, and without her knowing that Frank had returned the poor fellow was laid in his last bed in Burian Churchyard.

On the night of the funeral Nancy went, as was her custom, to lock the door of the house, and as was her custom too, she looked out into the night. At this instant a horseman rode up in hot haste, called her by name and hailed her in a voice that made her blood boil. The voice was Frank's! She could never forget that voice; and the horse she now saw was her sweetheart's favorite colt. He had often ridden him when he came to see her at Alsia Mill. The rider was imperfectly seen; but he looked very sorrowful and deadly pale. Still Nancy knew him to be Frank Lenine.

He told her that he had just arrived home, and that the first moment he was at liberty he had taken horse to fetch his loved one and to make her his bride. Nancy's excitement was so great that she was easily persuaded to spring on the horse behind him, that they might reach his home before the morning. When she took Frank's hand, a cold shiver passed through her, and as she grasped his waist to secure herself in her seat, her arm became as stiff as ice. She lost all power of speech and was terribly frightened, yet she knew not why. The moon had arisen and now burst out in a full flood of light, which poured through the heavy clouds that had obscured it. The horse pursued its journey with great rapidity, and whenever in weariness it slackened its speed the peculiar voice of the rider aroused its drooping energies. Beyond this no word was spoken.

They now came to Trove Bottom, where there was no bridge at that time. They dashed into the river. The moon shone full in their faces. Nancy looked into the stream and saw that the rider was in a shroud and other grave clothes. She now knew that she was being carried away by a spirit. Yet she had no power to save herself; indeed, the inclination to do so did not exist.

On went the horse at a furious pace until they came to the blacksmith's shop near Burian Church-town, when she knew by the light from the forge fire thrown across the road that the smith was still at his labors. She now recovered her speech. "Save me! save me! save me!" she cried with all her might.

The smith sprang from the door of the smithy with a red-hot iron in his hand, and as the horse rushed by, caught Nancy's dress and pulled her to the ground. The spirit, however, also seized her dress in a viselike grasp, and Nancy and the smith were dragged along as far as the old almshouses, near the churchyard. Here the horse for a moment stopped. The smith seized that moment and with his hot iron burned off the dress from the dead rider's hand, thus saving Nancy, more dead than alive, while the specter bridegroom passed over the churchyard wall and vanished on the grave in which Frank had been laid but a few hours before.

The smith took Nancy into his shop, and he soon aroused some of his neighbors, who carried the poor girl to her home. Her parents laid her on her bed. She spoke no word but to ask for her child, request that they give it up to Frank's parents and express her desire to be buried in Frank's grave. Before the morning light fell on the world, Nancy had breathed her last breath.

A horse was seen that night to pass through the church-town like a ball from a musket, and in the morning Frank's colt was found dead in Bernowhall Cliff, covered with foam, its eyes forced from its head and its swollen tongue hanging out of its mouth. On Frank's grave was found the piece of Nancy's dress which was left in the spirit's hand when the smith burned her from his grasp.

It is said that one or two of the sailors who survived the wreck related after the funeral how on Allhallows Eve Frank had been like one mad; they could hardly keep him on the ship. He seemed more asleep than awake, and after great excitement he fell as if dead upon the deck and lay so for hours. When he came to himself, he told them that he had been taken to the village of Kimyall, and that if he ever married the woman who had cast the spell, he would make her suffer the longest day she had to live for drawing his soul out of his body.

Poor Nancy was buried in her lover's grave, and her companion in sowing hemp seed, who saw the white coffin, slept beside her within the year.

ఆనీు౨ఆనీు౨

24. In the Magic Mountains

A HUNTER killed a stag in the mountains and began to skin it. He then hung the skin on a bush and went down to a stream to wash the blood from his hands. When he came back, he found to his surprise that the dead stag had come to life and was bounding away. When he had recovered from his astonishment, he chased the beast but could not overtake it, and it was soon lost to sight.

He met a wayfarer, briefly told him the story and asked if he had ever seen a stag without a skin. "I have never seen a stag without a skin, but I do not wonder at your story. Near here there is a healing spring where any beast, even if wounded unto death, can be cured by bathing. Your stag probably bathed there and is now sound and well. But if you want to know more about this wonderful country of ours, seek out a man called Dervish, and he will tell you things that will soon make you forget all about the stag."

"Where can I find this Dervish?" asked the hunter.

"Go from village to village and look into every courtyard, and when you see a man smoking a pipe, with an ass and a she-ass bound before him, ask him."

The hunter went away and after a long search found Dervish, who told him the following story.

"I was married," said Dervish, "and loved my wife, but she deceived me with my next-door neighbor. When I heard of this, I questioned my wife, but instead of answering she struck me with a whip. To my horror, I was turned into a dog. My wife drove me out into the yard, and for shame I ran away.

"On the road I suffered hunger, thirst and despair. For the first time in my life I knew what it was to be powerless, and realized what a great difference there is between man and beast. When I opened my mouth and tried to speak, I only barked and howled. I tried to stand on my hind legs and walk like a man, but I fell either backwards or forwards. Then I jumped about and did this so easily and briskly that I regained my spirits and came to think that even a dog's life had its pleasures.

"While I was merrily jumping, I unexpectedly saw a man. He looked at me and I at him. The man smiled and I ran up to him, but he was afraid and lifted his stick to strike me. We both moved away from each other. I wanted to speak but only barked, and the man raised his stick again. Then I began to frolic and jump, and the man smiled again and let me come up to him. I understood how dog and man are always the best of friends, and in my mind I thanked my wicked wife that she had turned me into a dog and not some other beast, a pig, for instance.

"The man who beckoned me to come to him was a good village priest, and we soon became great friends. He caressed me, gave me something to eat, and I went away with him. The kindhearted priest, overcome by the heat, lay down to rest under a tree. I wished to do the same, but the priest said, 'Watch over me!' So I did not go to sleep, rightly thinking that if the priest woke and found me asleep, he would give me no more bread and perhaps would drive me away.

"Ah! the beginning of my dog life was grievous. In the evening the priest stopped to sleep with some shepherds who were watching their flocks. The shepherds, to show honor to their pastor, killed a lamb for supper, got wine and made merry. Though I took no direct part in the feast, I kept close behind my master. After supper one of the shepherds looked at me and said, 'This dog must be fond of wine, for he never takes his eyes from the glass and now and then licks his lips.' I nodded my head several times. Then the shepherds poured me out some wine in a plate, and I lapped it up with pleasure.

"When they were all asleep, wolves came and attacked the sheep. The shepherds' dogs barked but did not dare attack the wolves. I rose and killed three wolves on the spot. When the shepherds saw this, they offered the priest a good price for me, and he finally sold me. Before long I had killed a vast number of wolves, and the fame of me reached the ears of the king of the country. I was brought and taken to the palace, to the sick daughter of the king, who was tormented by female nightmare spirits.

"Every morning the princess woke exhausted and enfeebled. On the first night of my watch I saw ugly swans enter the bed-chamber through the closed doors. They choked and trampled upon the sleeping princess. I was chained up and could do nothing to help the poor maiden. In the morning I was scolded for not having done anything, but one of the courtiers de-fended me, saying, 'He is a good dog, but he must be un-chained, and then we shall see what he can do.'

"The next night the swans came again. I killed ten of them, but the eleventh begged me to spare her, saying she would help me in the matter of my wife and our neighbor. I trusted the swan and let her go.

"To my delight the princess rose healthy and merry next

morning. The king was exceedingly pleased with me and ordered me to have a heavy gold chain and to be fed right royally. I lived well in the palace, but I longed to see my home and wife again, so I ran away.

"When I entered my own house, my wife took off my gold chain, struck me with her whip and turned me into a duck. I flew into a field near by where millet had been sown, and being inexperienced, was caught at once in nets laid by a peasant. The peasant took me under his arm and gave me to his wife, telling her to cook me for dinner. As soon as the peasant had gone out, the woman looked at me intently and then took down a whip from the wall. She struck me with the whip and turned me into a man again. 'Have I helped you or not?' she asked. 'We were twelve sisters. You killed ten of us. I am the eleventh, and your wife is the twelfth. Now go home, take the whip which hangs over your wife's bed, strike her and your neighbor with it, and you can turn them into any kind of beast that you wish.'

"I went in late at night, when my wife and the neighbor were both asleep, and I struck them with the whip and turned my wife into a jackass and the man into a she-ass, and here they are."

The hunter was terrified when he heard this story of Dervish. He ran away from the enchanted mountain realm as fast as he could and resolved never to go back there again.

25. The Frog's Skin

THERE WERE ONCE three brothers who wished to marry. They said, "Let us each shoot an arrow, and each shall take his wife from the place the arrow falls." They shot their arrows. Those of the two brothers fell on noblemen's houses, while the youngest brother's arrow fell in a lake. The two elder brothers led home their noble wives, and the youngest went to the shore of the lake. He saw a frog creep out of the lake and sit down upon a stone. He took it up and carried it back to the house. All the brothers came home with what fate had given them: the elder brothers with the noble maidens, and the youngest with a frog.

The brothers went out to work; the wives prepared the dinner and attended to all their household duties. The frog sat by the fire croaking, and its eyes glittered. Thus they lived together a long time in love and harmony.

At last the sisters-in-law wearied of the sight of the frog. When they swept the house, they threw out the frog with the dust. If the youngest brother found it, he took it up in his hand. If not, the frog would leap back to its place by the fire and begin to croak. The noble sisters did not like this and said to their husbands, "Drive this frog out and get a real wife for your brother." Every day the brothers bothered the youngest. He replied saying, "This frog is certainly my fate. I am worthy of no better; I must be faithful to it." His sisters-in-law persisted in telling their husbands that the brother and his frog must be sent away, and at last they agreed.

The young brother was now left quite desolate. There was no one to make his food, no one to stand watching at the door. For a short time a neighboring woman came to wait upon him, but she had no time, so he was left alone. The man became very melancholy.

Once when he was thinking sadly of his loneliness, he went to work. When he had finished his day's labor, he went home. He looked into his house and was struck with amazement. The sideboard was well replenished. In one place was spread a cloth, and on the cloth were many different kinds of tempting viands. He looked and saw the frog in its place croaking. He said to himself that his sisters-in-law must have done this for him, and went to work again. He was out all day working, and when he came home he always found everything prepared for him.

Once he said to himself, "I will see for once who is this unseen benefactor who comes to do good to me and look after me." That day he stayed at home. He seated himself on the roof of the house and watched. In a short time the frog leaped out of the fireplace, jumped over to the doors and all around the room. Seeing no one there, it went back and took off its frog's skin, put it near the fire and came forth a beautiful maiden, fair as the sun. So lovely was she that man could not imagine anything prettier. In the twinkling of an eye she had tidied everything, prepared the food and cooked it. When everything was ready, she went to the fire, put on her skin again and began to croak.

When the man saw this, he was very much astonished. He rejoiced exceedingly that God had granted him such happiness.

He descended from the roof, went in, caressed his frog tenderly, and then sat down to his tasty supper.

The next day the man hid himself in the place where he had been the day before. The frog, having satisfied itself that nobody was there, stripped off its skin and began its good work. This time the man stole silently into the house, seized the frog's skin in his hand and threw it into the fire. When the maiden saw this, she entreated him, she wept—said she, "Do not burn it or you will surely be destroyed." But the man had burned it in a moment. "Now if your happiness be turned to misery, it is not my fault," said the sorrow-stricken woman.

In a very short time the whole countryside knew that the man who had a frog now possessed in its place a lovely woman who had come to him from heaven.

The lord of the country heard of this and wished to take her from him. He called the beautiful woman's husband to test him and said, "Sow a barnful of wheat in a day or give me your wife." When he had spoken thus, the man was obliged to consent, and he went home melancholy.

When he went in, he told his wife what had taken place. She reproached him, saying, "I told you what would happen if you burned the skin, and you did not heed me, but I will not blame you. Be not sad. Go in the morning to the edge of the lake from which I came and call out, 'Mother and Father! I pray you, lend me your swift bullocks.' Lead them away with you and they will in one day plow the fields and sow the grain." The husband did this.

He went to the edge of the lake and called out, "Mother and Father! I entreat you to lend me your swift bullocks today." There came forth from the lake such a team of oxen as was never seen on sea or land. The youth drove the oxen to his lord's fields and they plowed and sowed them in one day.

His lord was very much surprised. He did not know if there was anything impossible to this man whose wife he wanted. He called him a second time and said, "Go and gather up the wheat you have sown, that not a grain may be wanting and that the barn be full. If you do not do this, your wife is mine."

"This is impossible," said the man to himself. He went home to his wife, who again reproached him, and then said, "Go to the lake and ask for the jackdaws."

He went to the lake and called out, "Mother and Father! I beg you to lend me your jackdaws today." From the lake came forth flocks of jackdaws. They flew to the plowed ground; each gathered up a seed and put it in the barn.

The lord came and cried out, "There is one seed short. I know each one, and one is missing." At that moment a jackdaw's caw was heard. It came with the missing seed but owing to a lame foot was a little late.

The lord was very angry that even the impossible was possible to this man, and could not think what to give him to do. He puzzled his brain until he thought of the following plan. He called the man and said to him, "My mother, who died in this village, took with her a ring. If you will go to the other world and bring that ring hither to me, it is well. If not, I shall take away your wife."

The man said to himself, "This is utterly impossible." He went home and complained to his wife. She reproached him and then said, "Go to the lake and ask for the ram." The husband went and called out, "Mother and father! give me your ram today, I pray you." From the lake there came forth a ram with twisted horns. From his mouth issued a flame of fire. He said to the man, "Mount on my back."

The man jumped astride him, and as quick as lightning the ram descended toward the lower regions. He went on and shot like an arrow through the earth. They traveled on and saw in one place a man and woman sitting on a bullock's skin, which was not enough for them, and they were like to fall off. The man called out to them, "What can be the meaning of this, that this bullock skin is not big enough for two people?" They said, "We have seen many pass like you, but none has returned. When you come back we shall answer your question."

They went on their way and saw a man and woman sitting on an ax handle, and they were not afraid of falling. The man called out to them, "Are you not afraid of falling from the handle of the ax?" They said to him, "We have seen many pass by like you, but none has returned. When you come back we shall answer your question."

They went on their way again until they came to a place where they saw a priest feeding cattle. The priest had such a long beard that it spread over the ground, and the cattle instead of eating grass fed on the priest's beard, and he could not prevent it. The man called out, "Priest, what is the meaning of this? Why is your beard pasture for the cattle?" The priest replied, "I have seen many pass by like you, but none has returned. When you come back, I shall answer your question."

They journeyed on again until they came to a place where they saw nothing but boiling pitch, and a flame came forth from it. And this was hell! The ram said, "Sit firmly on my back, for we must pass through this fire." The man held fast, the ram gave a leap and they escaped through the fire unhurt.

They saw a melancholy woman seated on a gold throne. She said, "What is it, my child? What troubles you? What has brought you here?" He told her everything that had happened to him. She said, "I must punish this very wicked child of mine, and you must take him a casket from me." She gave him a casket and said, "Whatever you do, do not open this casket yourself. Take it with you, give it to your lord and run quickly away from him."

The man took the casket and went away. He came to the place where the priest was feeding the cattle. The priest said, "I promised you an answer. Hearken unto my words. In life I loved nothing but myself. I cared for naught else. My flocks I fed on other pastures than my own, and the neighboring cattle died of starvation. Now I am paying the penalty."

Then he went on to the place where the man and woman were sitting on the handle of the ax. They said, "We promised you an answer. Hearken unto our words. We loved each other too well on earth, and it is the same with us here."

Then he came to the two seated on the bullock's skin which was not big enough for them. They said, "We promised you an answer. Hearken unto our words. We despised each other in life, and we equally despise each other here."

At last the man came up on earth, descended from the ram and went to his lord. He gave him the casket and quickly ran away. The lord opened the casket, and there came forth fire which swallowed him up. Our brother was thus victorious over his enemy, and no one took his wife from him. They lived lovingly together and blessed God as their deliverer.

❧❦❧❦

26. The Man with the Evil Eye

THERE WAS once upon a time a rich gentleman who lived in a fine house on the banks of the Vistula. All the windows in the house looked towards the river; none looked towards the wide sweep of the country around. The path under the poplars which led up to the house was overgrown with grass and weeds and showed plainly enough that none of the neighbors visited there, and that very little of the old hospitality was to be experienced there.

The gentleman who owned the house had lived there for seven years and had come from some far-off place. The peasants knew little about him, and they avoided him with fear and trembling, for there were terrible tales about him.

The gentleman was born on the banks of the river Sau, and his parents had been rich. Misfortune, however, had pursued him from the cradle upwards. He had an evil eye, which scattered disease and death wherever its glances fell. If he by ill chance glanced over his herd, the cattle on which his eye fell died. Whatever he loved would surely die. His own parents, to complete the son's sorrow, perished, and the man with the evil eye, as he came to be called in his birthplace, where the evil eye had caused so much mischief, sold everything he had and set off to the banks of the Vistula, where he bought the fine house. He kept no folk about him save one old manservant, who had nursed him in his arms when he was a boy and on whom the evil eye of his master had no effect.

The unlucky man seldom went out of his house, for he knew that his glance brought misfortune, disease and death on what it lighted on. When he did go out in his carriage, his old servant sat beside him and told him when they were coming to a man, a village or a town. Then the miserable man would either cover his eyes with his hands or cast down his glances on the floor of his carriage, where he always had a bundle of pea stalks at his feet, for when the evil eye is directed to a bundle of pea stalks it does no damage but merely dries up the stalks.

So it was that he had all the windows of his fine house made to look over the Vistula. Twice had he by ill chance looked upon his farm buildings, and they had been set on fire by his glance.

In spite of all his care the sailors cursed him and pointed with fear to the wide windows of his beautiful house out of which he scattered destruction amongst them, the stream rushing on fast in the channel and bringing many a ship to ground opposite the White House, as the place was called.

One boatman determined to see the man. He jumped into his boat and set off to the house. When he arrived there he asked to see the master. The old servant, fearful of the consequences, led him into the room. His master was dining, and being put out that he should be interrupted at his meal, he frowned upon the stranger. Immediately a fever took the sailor, and he sank down on the floor at the door.

At the command of his master the old servant took the man to his boat, gave him some money and rowed him back to the other side of the river. The poor sailor was ill for a long time, and when he regained his strength he gave such a terrible account of the White House, and of its master, as greatly increased the fear of his comrades. From that time, when they went down the river in their boats and came opposite to the White House, they would turn their eyes away and pray heartily that they might be protected from the evil glance of the terrible man who lived there.

Three years passed and the White House was still the dread of the neighbors and the terror of the sailors. No one came to see the much-feared man, and he lived solitary and miserable. The next winter was very severe. The wolves, coming together, howled with hunger around the house, and the master sat by the hearth, on which burned a large fire, and sorrowfully turned over the leaves of a large book. The old servant had secured all the doors and sat at the other side of the room warming himself, and busied in mending a fishing net.

"Stanislas," said his master, "have you caught any fish?"

"Not many, master, but as many as we two shall want."

"That is true," said his master. "Although so many years have passed, we are but two. O unlucky hour in which I was born! Here I am alone, and all men fly from me as if I were a monster." And the tears fell in a torrent from his unfortunate eyes.

All of a sudden they heard a voice crying for help. The master started. It was a long time since he had heard a strange voice. The old servant rushed out, and his master followed him with the light in his hand.

Before the door stood a covered sledge, and by it was an old man who called for help. As soon as the stranger saw the two men coming to him, he lifted his wife, who had fainted, out of the sledge, and the old servant helped the terrified daughter, a beautiful girl, to alight.

They put more wood on the fire and brought the fainted lady

round, and the master of the house, pleased to be able to show hospitality, went and fetched some old wine in order to drink the strangers' healths. The old servant laughed to himself as he marked his master's joyful face. The strange guests, cheered by the wine, told how they had lost their way, how they had fallen in with a pack of hungry wolves, and how their fleet horse had carried them to the White House. The luggage was now taken out of the sledge, and the wearied travelers retired to rest in warm, comfortable chambers. All was still in the White House, save that the fire now and then sent forth a glimmering flame.

It was within an hour of midnight, and the old servant was asleep by the fireside, when the door of his master's bed-chamber opened and the unhappy man trod lightly into the hall. Stanislas, wondering whether he was dreaming, rubbed his eyes and said, "What, cannot my master sleep?"

"Be quiet, old friend!" said his master in a joyful voice. "I cannot sleep and do not wish to sleep when I am so happy as I now am." And he sat down in a big armchair by the fireside, smiled and commenced to weep.

"Weep, poor master, weep," said Stanislas to himself. "Maybe you may weep your evil eyes away."

"Would that God would give me what I now wish," said his master, "and I would ask for nothing more in the world. Here have I lived all these years like a hermit or a criminal, and yet I have never willingly hurt anyone, and my soul is free from sin—but my eyes, my eyes!"

His countenance, which was so happy till now, became gloomy as usual; but soon a smile appeared on his face as hope once more chased away sorrow.

"Dear friend!" said he, and Stanislas looked at him, "maybe I shall marry."

"Heaven help us!" cried the old servant; "but where then is your future bride?" The master rose from his chair, walked on tiptoe to the side door which led to the chambers where the travelers slept, and pointing to the door, said, "There."

Stanislas nodded his head as if he approved of his master's choice and cheerfully put some wood upon the fire. His master went back to his room in deep thought, and the servant mumbled to himself, "Heaven grant it! But pears don't grow on willow trees." And soon he was asleep.

On the following morning the traveler rose rested and refreshed, but he was not able to continue his journey in consequence of the illness of his wife. The master of the house was pleased when he heard that the strangers must pass some more days in his house, and old Stanislas began almost to think that pears might grow on willows after all.

The stranger was not exactly rich, but he had enough, and was deemed an honest man, and lived honorably. He was much pleased with his friendly host, and as he was one day talking to his wife, who had much improved in her health, he said, "Margaret, it strikes me that our host is in love with our daughter Mary, and from what I can see, I think she does not dislike him. I cannot but be pleased with it."

"Oh," said his wife, "you only imagine it." But she was secretly pleased that her husband had no objection to what she had herself very much wished. "The man is not poor; he has lived here a long time, and he has proved himself a gentleman," went on the husband, walking up and down the room, "and our daughter is old enough to be married and take on her the cares of a household."

In the evening the husband, having partaken of the host's good wine, stroked his gray mustache with satisfaction and listened with joy when the master of the house asked for his daughter's hand.

"My brother," said he after a short pause, "I am pleased with you, and since you ask no dowry with my daughter and you have enough to live upon, she shall be your wife."

Three months later Mary and her parents returned to the White House for the wedding. The grass and weeds were cleared from the avenue of poplars, and many horses and carriages passed along it to and fro, as relatives and friends of the beautiful girl came in troops to see her married. In a few days, however, all was still and deserted again and fresh grass and weeds began to grow in the avenue under the poplars.

The winter was at hand, and the inmates of the White House only numbered one more—the mistress of the house— for most of the servants whom the master had engaged ran away at once as soon as they heard that he had an evil eye. And those who stayed awhile, having been taken ill, soon left the house also. The young, beautiful wife lay ill upon her rich bed. Near her was her husband, who, with averted eyes, pressed her cold hand.

The poor wife knew well how terrible was her husband's glance. She knew that through it her suffering and sorrow were increased; but still, in her love for the sorrowing man, she asked him to look upon her once more.

"My Mary," said the wretched man, with a deep sigh, "I shall never be happy with you so long as I have my eyes. Cut them out then. Here is a sharp knife, and at your hand it will cause me no pain."

The poor woman shuddered at this terrible proposal, and

the wretched man sank from his chair to the floor and began to weep bitterly.

"Of what use is this gift of Heaven to me?" cried he. "Of what use is it to me to possess the pleasures men have in sight when my eyes scatter destruction and ruin around? You are ill, my Mary. Why, a tree itself would wither when I cast my glance upon it in an evil hour. Take courage, though. Upon our child these eyes shall never look. Him they shall never harm, and he shall not have reason to curse his father."

A groan was the only answer of the sick wife. The master called in a servant and left the room. All at once two different cries were heard from the two opposite sides of the White House. From one side came the cry of a newborn child; from the other, in the hall where the fire burned, came the cry of a man in pain. The one was the cry of an infant as it looked upon the light for the first time; the other was the cry of a man who had bid farewell to sight forever.

Six years later there were windows in the White House from which one could obtain a fine view of the village and the surrounding country. The sailors had begun to make the house a resting place on their way down the stream. The mistress was well and merry, and her great joy was a beautiful little daughter who led the blind father about. The countryfolk who had fled in terror from the miserable man now came up to him in friendship, when they saw him blind and taking a walk led by his little daughter. The former stillness departed. The servants filled the once empty halls of the White House.

Old Stanislas had on that terrible day buried his master's eyes in the garden. One day he wondered what had become of them, and whether he could find them. So he dug for them. All of a sudden the eyes glared on him with a bright light.

Hardly had the glance fallen on his face when he stumbled, and falling to the ground, died.

That was the first time the evil eyes had done him hurt, and it was the last time their power was exerted. They had done him no hurt while his master kept them, because, as he loved his servant, his heart had destroyed their power. Now that they were in the earth they had acquired power for fresh evil and killed the honest old man!

His blind master sorrowed long for him, and over his grave he placed a fine cross, near which the sailors often offered up a prayer when they landed at the White House.

ঌৡৡৠ৵ঌৡৡৠ৵

27. *The Cat-Woman*

ONE WINTER EVE some villagers of Des Riais had gathered to tell and listen to stories about sorcerers, ghosts and *loups-garous*. When it came to Père Pichard's turn to spin a yarn, he knocked out his pipe against the knucklebone of his thumb and asked, "Which story do you want?"

"The tale of the cat-woman," came from all sides.

"Very well," he said. "But it isn't a tale but a true story, and I shall tell it to you just as it happened, without keeping back or changing anything." And this is what he told:

When I was courting my wife I went to and fro on the Croix-des-Haies road, which got its name from the calvary standing at a crossroads midway between her house and mine.

One night I stayed at my sweetheart's house later than usual. In those days there was a great happiness in my heart, and I sang as I walked toward home. When I came to the crossroads, I was surprised to see a great white cat at the foot of the calvary. The beast walked right up to me, rubbed her back against my legs and meowed tenderly. Then she accompanied me as far as the edge of the village, where she jumped into a ditch and disappeared.

From that night on the cat met me at the crossroads and followed me home. I became so used to her that I paid her very little attention. And I forgot all about the animal after I married and had no further occasion for walking at night on the Croix-des-Haies road.

After five or six months of marriage I awoke one night towards midnight and found that my wife was not beside me. I was greatly astonished and called out, "Nanon! Nanon!" There was no response. I lit the candle and searched through the house. Nanon was not there. I found this very strange. Finally I returned to my bed and went back to sleep. When I awoke in the morning, Nanon was there in bed beside me.

"Where did you go last night?" I asked.

"Me?" said she, and her face turned red. But she would say no more.

I did not press her further then. That night, however, I was on the alert, and when she got out of bed about midnight I was aware of it. I glanced toward the door, and although the room was dark I was able to make out something that looked like a huge white cat, and it went out the door. At dawn Nanon returned to bed.

One morning as she was doing her housework, a spider fell down her neck. She ran to a closet to take off her clothing. I was curious, put my eye to the keyhole and saw a very odd thing. On her neck just above her left shoulder there was a red mark shaped like a cat's paw. I had heard it said that people who run as *garous* have a mark somewhere upon their bodies. Now that mark and Nanon's leaving the house at night convinced me that she was a cat-woman.

The realization that this was a fact had a terrible effect upon me. For many days I could hardly eat a thing, and for a long time I wandered about the fields like a man who had lost his mind. One day, I remember, I mustered up enough courage to ask her what that mark on her neck was. She refused to answer me, and as she walked away I saw that there was fury in her great glittering green eyes.

Now the cathole in the door was not large enough to admit a cat-woman of her size. As I always took care to bolt the door before going to bed, I wondered how she got back into the house after her nocturnal prowlings. Late one night when Nanon was away, I lit the candle and awaited her return. An hour or two after midnight I heard scratching at the door. Then I observed a paw come in the hole, reach up and pull back the bolt, and the door opened. I snuffed out the candle immediately, crept into bed and feigned sleep.

The next day I put a sharp edge on my short-handled ax. An hour before dawn I heard scratching at the door. In an instant I was there with my ax in my hand. When the paw appeared, I struck with all my might. I heard a piercing scream, a scream that still makes me shudder every time I think of it, although all this happened forty years ago. Nanon did not come near the house for three days. On the fourth day she came home. One of her hands was missing. After this she never went out at night. The cat-woman of Croix-des-Haies never prowled again.

ᴈᎶᏔᏎᎧᏎ

28. *The White Mouse*

ONCE THERE was a young man who lived in Hirschhorn, and each night a goblin came into his bedroom, pressed down so hard upon his breast that he could hardly breathe and caused him to have terrifying dreams. His mother was aware of this, and, not wishing to endure any more of it, sought a way to end it. She ordered her son to give her a signal the moment he was conscious of the presence of the goblin or nightmare in the room. Then that night she spread a white sheet over him as he lay in bed and hid herself nearby.

An hour or two after dark the goblin entered the room through the keyhole. Immediately after, the young man gave the signal. Then he fell into a kind of swoon and began to whimper and moan. His mother sprang to the bed and quickly snatched up the four corners of the sheet. Folding it tightly, she laid it in a dresser drawer, which she locked, leaving the key in the lock. Her son now drew a very deep breath, as if a hundred-pound weight had been lifted from his breast. By this his mother knew that she had succeeded in capturing the goblin.

That same night, or rather, early the next morning, a maiden died suddenly in Erbach. No one could say what kind of illness had stricken her. She was washed, dressed in her grave-clothes and laid on the bier, all ready to be carried to the graveyard.

Shortly afterwards it happened that the young man of

Hirschhorn, who by now had slept two nights without being tortured by the goblin, drew the key from the lock on the dresser drawer in which the folded sheet had been laid. Instantly a white mouse popped out of the keyhole and ran out the door. At that moment in Ehrbach they were about to close the maiden's coffin. But before the lid was down, a white mouse ran in the door, up a chair and leaped into the mouth of the dead girl. Immediately she came alive and opened her eyes wide. She was mightily surprised to find herself in a coffin.

⊷§§⊷⊷§§⊷

29. *The Clever Knight*

A CERTAIN noble knight, having grievously offended his king, sent messengers to the monarch to intercede for him; and they obtained his pardon, but on condition that he should appear at court and enter the king's palace on foot and on horseback at the same time; that is, half walking and half riding. Besides, he was to bring with him his best friend, his best buffoon and his worst enemy. When the knight got to thinking about how difficult it would be to fulfill these strange conditions, he became very much worried.

One night a pilgrim came to his door and asked for food and lodging, and the good man was admitted and entertained in hospitable fashion. Suddenly the knight had an idea. He took his wife aside and said, "I know these pilgrims often carry with them considerable sums of money. If you think fit, let us slay this fellow and take his money." "You say well," said the lady.

Very early in the morning when all were asleep, the knight awoke the pilgrim and sent him on his way. He then went out to the byre, slaughtered a bull calf and buried it. Afterward he roused his wife, and showing her a little money as if it had been taken from the murdered pilgrim, said, "I have done the deed and buried the body in the stable."

On the day when he had to appear before his liege lord, he took with him his great staghound, his wife, who was a rather large raw-boned woman with a bold face, and his unweaned child, as pretty a dimpled Cupid as ever was seen. As they drew near the royal palace, the knight put one leg over the dog's back, as if he were riding, while with the other he walked; and thus as a pedestrian and equestrian he entered the king's castle.

When the king observed his cunning, he was greatly surprised. "But," said he, "where is your best friend?" The knight then drew his sword and gave the staghound a smart blow with the flat of the blade. The hound fled howling away. The knight then called him back, and the noble animal turned and came back to his master. "Here," said he. "Here is the most faithful of all friends."

"True," said the king. "Now where is your buffoon?"

"Here," said the knight, pointing to his child. "I never have so much pleasure and laugh so heartily as when watching the antics of this moppet."

"Well and good," continued the king. "Where is your worst enemy?"

The knight quickly turned toward his wife, struck her on

the shoulder and cried, "Imprudent harlot, how dare you look wantonly upon the king?" The wife, furious at being struck and burning with indignation because of the false accusation, let out a shriek that could be heard a mile away. "Cursed murderer," cried she, "why did you strike me? Are you forgetting that in your own house you killed a poor pilgrim for the sake of a little gold?" "Wretch!" cried he, "is it nothing to you that you disgrace your child?"

Turning to the king and the gentlemen about him and brandishing her arms in rage, the wife said, "Come with me and I will show you where the body of the dead man lies buried in our stable." Search was accordingly made, and she told where the digging should be done. Great was her dismay and mighty the astonishment of all who were there when nothing came to light but a dead calf!

Recognizing in all this the wit of the knight, the nobles praised him highly, and ever after the king valued and honored him exceedingly.

❧❧❧

30. *Hackelnberg and the Screech Owl*

FAR AND WIDE in the Harz Mountains and the Thuringian Forest rides the wild huntsman Hackelnberg, although he prefers abiding in the Hakel, whence he has his name, particularly in the neighborhood of the Dummberg. With his dogs he is often to be heard at midnight riding in storm and

rain, or in moonlight when the sky is partially covered with
fleeting clouds, following in the air the shades of the game he
slaughtered in his lifetime. His usual course is from the Dummberg across the Hakel, to the present desolate village of Am-
mendorf. But only to a few Sunday's children (who are said
to possess the faculty of seeing specters) is granted the power
of seeing him.

To them he appears at times as a solitary huntsman with a
dog. At other times they see him in a carriage drawn by four
horses and accompanied by six hunting dogs. But everyone
may hear his terrific rushing through the air, the hollow baying
of his dogs and the plashing of his horse's hoofs, as if they
were passing through water. They hear his wild "Hu! hu!"
and see his companion and hornblower, the screech owl.

Three travelers were once sitting in the neighborhood of
the Dummberg. The night was far advanced; the moon peeped
forth between the fleeting clouds, and all around was still.
Suddenly a rushing noise was heard above their heads. They
looked up, and a large screech owl flew before them.

"Oh!" exclaimed one of the travelers, "that is the Tut-Ursel.
Then the wild huntsman Hackelnberg is not far off."

"Let us run," said the second, in a tremulous tone, "before
the specter overtakes us."

"Escape we cannot," said the third, "but you have nothing
to fear if you do not provoke him. Lie flat down, quite still,
on your faces while he passes over us. But you must not speak
to him or it may be with us as it was with that shepherd."

The travelers laid themselves down in the underwood and
soon heard around them a great noise as of a pack of hounds
forcing their way through the thicket, and above them a hollow sound as of game when pursued, intermingled with the

wild huntsman's appalling "Hu! hu!" Two of the travelers lay close to the ground, but the third could not resist his curiosity. He cast a sideward glance through the branches and saw the shadow of a huntsman, who with his dogs hurried over them. Everything was again still around. The travelers raised themselves slowly, and timidly they gazed after Hackelnberg. But he was gone and did not again appear.

After a long pause one of them asked, "Who or what is the Tut-Ursel?" His companion answered, "In a remote convent in Thuringia there once lived a nun of the name of Ursel. In her lifetime she was wont to annoy the sisterhood with her howling voice, and frequently disturbed the singing, on which account they called her the Tut-Ursel. But it was much worse after her death. Then every night at eleven o'clock she put her head through a hole in the tower that opened into the choir of the church and screamed mournfully. And every morning at four o'clock she joined in the choral song.

"For a day or two the sisters endured this with beating hearts and trembling knees. But on the fourth morning when she joined in the chant, one of the sisters whispered in a tremulous voice to her neighbor, 'Oh, that is certainly Ursel!' The chanting was suddenly stopped, their hair stood on end and all the nuns ran out of the church screaming, 'Oh, the Tut-Ursel! Tut-Ursel!' All the threats of punishment and penance were insufficient to induce them again to enter the sacred edifice until Ursel had been exorcised from within the convent walls. The most famous exorcist of his time, who resided in a Capuchin convent on the banks of the Danube, was sent for. By fasting and prayer he banished Ursel, in the form of a screech owl, to the distant Dummberg.

"Here she met with Hackelnberg and found in his wild cry

of 'Hu! hu!' as much pleasure as he did in her 'U! hu!' And now, united forever, they go forth on their aerial hunt, he pleased at having found a being to his liking, she not less delighted at being no longer confined within the convent walls listening to the echo of the nuns' chant."

"Now we have heard the story of Tut-Ursel," said one of the travelers. "Tell us what happened to the shepherd who spoke to Hackelnberg."

"Listen to the wonderful tale," answered his companion. "A shepherd once heard the wild huntsman riding just over his pens and set his dogs after him, calling out, 'Good luck, Hackelnberg!' Hackelnberg instantly turned and cried with a hollow thundering voice, 'As thou hast helped me to hunt, thou shalt have some of the game.' The shepherd crouched down trembling. Hackelnberg flung down a half-devoured thigh bone of a horse, which smote him as he sat in his sheep cart so severely that he has never since been able to hold himself upright, or to move backwards or forwards."

ക്ষൂ≫·ക്ഷൂ≫

31. The Devil in Skirts

BALDUIN, the Count of Flanders, could have married Beatrice, daughter of the King of France, but he spurned the offer, a foolish act that could have sprung from naught but monstrous pride. He did not want her, yet apparently he did not want anyone else to have her, and when the Emperor of

Constantinople came and obtained her father's permission to marry her, the count's feelings were so badly hurt that he left the French court and went to Noyon, where he remained for three days. On the fourth day he felt a great longing to go hunting. He summoned his hunting companions and bid them bring the hounds, and all set off for the forest.

And they encountered a mighty boar, as black as hell and as strong as a lion. When he heard the baying of the hounds, he fled, and the hunters spurred after him. From time to time he would make a stand and kill some of the count's best dogs. This angered the count mightily, and he swore he would not turn back until he had killed him. The beast now made for the forest of Morman. The count followed, crossing the Seine and passing Vermandois. Seeking a refuge where he could hide and rest awhile, the black boar sped on. But the count, who had outdistanced all his companions, was too close behind. Leaping from his horse and advancing his great spear, the count cried, "Hold, you beast; you must now fight with Balduin."

The boar rushed at the count, who ran the spear right through the beast's heart and slew him. Then the count sat down upon the carcass. A strange mood fell upon him and he wondered what was delaying his comrades. When after a few minutes he looked up, he saw a maiden making her way through the trees toward him. She was quite alone, rode on a black ambler and was as pretty as an angel. He strode toward her, and seizing her horse's bridle, said, "Lady, I am very glad to see you."

In a soft voice she greeted him, and he asked, "Lady, why do you ride all alone and without companions?"

"Count," she answered in a voice as sweet as honey, "because Almighty God so wills it. My father, a king of the Orient, endeavored to force me to wed against my will and I ran away. I made a vow I never would marry a man unless he was the richest man in Christendom. Some of my servants fled with me, but fearing that they might get the notion of forcing me to return home, I slipped away from them. I swear I will not return until I have found the Count of Flanders, whom I have so often heard praised."

"Fair maid," said he, "I am the Count of Flanders whom you seek. In France I am the richest man, and I rule over fourteen counties. You have sought and found me. I ask you to be my wife."

These words were very pleasing to the damsel. But she was not sure that he was really the Count of Flanders. "There can be no doubt, dear lady, about my being the count," said he, and he was quite vexed that his companions did not arrive to tell her who he was.

"Lady, what is your name, who is your father and where is his domain?" he asked.

"My Christian name is Helius," she replied, "but I cannot disclose the name of my father. You must not ask me why, for God has ordered it so, and it cannot be otherwise."

The count blew a blast on his horn to summon his companions. Then came the Count of Valenciennes, Gaultier of Saint-Omer and many others. The first asked him if he had been successful in the chase. "Yes," answered the count. "I have killed the finest boar in the world, and God has sent me the beautiful maiden you see before you. I intend to make her my wife." At that Henry of Valenciennes inspected the maid very closely. She was clad in resplendent raiment, and nothing could be finer than the sleek ambler she sat on.

Nevertheless he did not approve of Balduin's sudden decision to marry the damsel. "How do you know who she is?" he asked. "Doubtless she is one who may be purchased with gold. Why not live with her as long as she pleases you and then let her go? A nobleman of your rank must act wisely and with due caution. Curses upon that terrible pride of yours that moved you to refuse marriage with the daughter of the King of France."

"Spoken like a sage," cried Balduin, "but it is the wish of my heart to wed this maid. No more advice from you; I forbid it."

These words troubled his companions sorely. The count now departed with the maiden, taking with him the boar's head. At Cameryk he married her, and there was a great wedding celebration. They had two daughters: one was christened Joanna and the other Margareta. However, the countess did not make many friends. The people hated her and blamed the count for listening to her evil counsels. During the fourteen years they lived together she caused crushing taxes to be levied upon the people and secretly encouraged the evil men in the land to commit foul crimes. Although she attended church and listened to the divine service, and even received the sacrament, she always departed before the elevation of the host. The people wondered about this and were full of suspicion.

In these days the Emperor of Constantinople was in great distress, for the Sultan of Sura with one hundred thousand Saracens had laid siege to Constantinople and ravaged the land. The emperor, calling upon his friends and allies for help, assembled some forty thousand Christians. One day he made a sally against the Saracens and was killed in the fray. His soldiers carried him back into the city and buried him with great honors. They were cast down and feared greatly that they would not be able to hold out against the besiegers very much longer. Acquillan the Sultan swore he would not retreat until he had taken the city, no matter how well it was defended.

At this time Balduin was in Flanders with Helius, his wife. On Easter Day in the year of grace 1188 he gave a great banquet in his palace at Vymandable. It was his custom on this day to invite all the nobility to a magnificent feast. Now when it came time to sit down to the banquet, there came before him a hermit who must have been at least a hundred years old. He leaned heavily upon a staff. And he asked for a dinner in God's name. The count graciously invited him in and ordered a servant to set a plate before him at a separate table in the banquet hall.

The count's wife had not yet come in, but she entered soon and sat down beside her husband, as was her custom. The instant the hermit set eyes on her, he began to tremble with fear. He crossed himself over and over and could neither eat nor drink. When the woman caught sight of the hermit, a look of extreme displeasure came upon her face. Soon this changed to fear, for she instinctively felt this man might bring her great misfortune. So she requested the count to order him to leave. "He is a cunning man," she said, "who knows more sleights than anyone. I cannot bear to look upon him. Therefore I beg you to remove him elsewhere."

"Wife," said the count, "it is good to give charity to those who ask for it. It is my wish that the hermit be served here today and refresh himself." The hermit heard this and his heart was full of gratitude.

"Dear man," the count asked him, "why do you not eat? Do not hesitate to tell me if there is something not upon your table which you desire. No matter what it is, you shall have it."

Thereupon the hermit rose up, and, addressing all the banqueters, told them that they ought to cease eating and drinking because they were in the presence of great danger. "In a moment," he said, "you will see something that will frighten you and chill your blood. But you will not be harmed if you put your trust in God."

These remarks caused universal wonder. The laughter and eating suddenly ceased. The hermit then began to utter the words of an exorcism. "Devil," he cried, "you who dwell in the body of this woman, I conjure you by Him who died on the cross, and who drove you and all the others, who with Lucifer sinned the sin of pride, out of Paradise, to come forth. Confess to all present how you seduced the Count of Flanders. When you have done this, fly back whither you came, and in your going do not touch anyone here with your hurtful hand."

The woman had no defense against this exorcism. And when she perceived she could no longer torment the count and the people of Flanders but had to go away, she began to speak.

"I am," she said, "one of the angels God cast out of Heaven. We who fell suffer horribly—more than you can imagine. Why blame us if we try to better our wretched condition? We wish every man to sin as we have sinned so that God in forgiving men's transgressions will also forgive us. When the count here sinned the sin of pride and refused to wed the daughter of the King of France, he left the way open for us to attack him. God then permitted me to enter the corpse of the daughter of an Oriental king. The maid had been the most beautiful ever seen. One night I entered her body and raised it up. And she has no other soul but me, for her soul has departed. The count was powerless to resist my advances and could not avoid marrying me. For fourteen years I caused him to lead an evil life, and I have made his people suffer. And it would have been worse had not the count remembered often to think on his Creator and to cross himself when he went to bed and when he arose in the morning. I had no power over either of his daughters because he had them baptized. More than this I shall not tell. I now fly to the Orient to bring this borrowed body to its grave."

As she said this, she left through a window, carrying away in her flight a little mullion. She harmed no one. The banqueters were stunned with wonder and fear. They withdrew from the table. The count bowed his head before the hermit and begged him to advise him what to do. The good man counseled him to go to the Pope and ask forgiveness for his sins. Then the hermit departed.

For three days the count was sunk in deep thought in his palace. On the fourth day he went to Brugge. There the people pointed the finger at him and jeered. The children cried, "Run away, for there is the count who married the devil." And the same happened at Ghent and Arras. So he made a vow to go to Jerusalem. He arranged his affairs and traveled first to Rome. There the Pope received him courteously, according him great honors. Never was mortal man more amazed than when the Pope heard the count's confession. The penance he gave was to go to Constantinople and assist with all his might the noble, widowed empress, the daughter of the King of France, whose city was beset by the Saracens. So the good Pope forgave all of Balduin's sins, and the count set out for Constantinople.

32. Lady Good Luck

A LONG, LONG while ago there lived a rajah and ranee who had only one daughter, and she was the most beautiful princess in the world. Her face was as fair and delicate as the clear moonlight, and they called her Sodewa Bai (Lady Good Luck). At her birth her father and mother had sent for all the wise men in the kingdom to tell her fortune, and they predicted that she would grow up richer and more fortunate than any other lady. And so it was, for from her earliest youth she was good and lovely, and whenever she opened her lips to speak, pearls and precious stones fell upon the ground, and as she walked along they would scatter on either side of her path. Her father soon became the richest rajah in all that country, for his daughter could not go across the room without shaking down jewels worth a dowry. Moreover, Sodewa Bai was born with a golden necklace about her neck, concerning which also her parents consulted astrologers, who said, "This is no common child. The necklace of gold about her neck contains your daughter's soul. Let it therefore be guarded with the utmost care, for if it were taken off and worn by another person, she would die." So the ranee, her mother, caused it to be firmly fastened round the child's neck, and as soon as she was old enough to understand, instructed her concerning its value, and bade her on no account ever allow it to be taken off.

At the time my story begins this princess was fourteen years old; but she was not married, for her father and mother had promised that she should not do so until it pleased herself; and although many great rajahs and nobles sought her hand, she constantly refused them all.

Now Sodewa Bai's father, on one of her birthdays, gave her a lovely pair of slippers, made of gold and jewels. Each slipper was worth a hundred thousand gold mohurs. There were none like them in all the earth. Sodewa Bai prized these slippers very much and always wore them when she went out walking, to protect her tender feet from the stones. But one day as she was wandering with her ladies upon the side of the mountain on which the palace was built, playing and picking the wild flowers, her foot slipped and one of the golden slippers fell down, down, down the steep hill slope, over rocks and stones, into the jungle below. Sodewa Bai sent attendants to search for it, and the rajah caused criers to go throughout the town and proclaim that whoever discovered the princess' slipper should receive a great reward. But though it was hunted for far and near, high and low, it could not be found.

It chanced, however, that not very long after this a young prince, the eldest son of a rajah who lived in the plains, was out hunting, and in the jungle he picked up the very little golden slipper which Sodewa Bai had lost, and which had tumbled all the way from the mountainside into the depths of the forest. He took it home with him and showed it to his mother, saying, "What a fairy foot must have worn this tiny slipper!" "Ah, my boy," she said, "this must in truth have belonged to a lovely princess (if she is but as beautiful as her slipper!); would that you could find such a one to be your wife!" Then they sent into all the towns of the kingdom to inquire for the owner of the lost slipper; but she could not be found. At last when many months had gone by it happened that news was brought by travelers to the rajah's capital of how, in a far distant land, very high among the mountains, there lived a beautiful princess who had lost her slipper, and whose father had offered a great reward to whoever should restore it. And from the description they gave, all were assured it was the one that the prince had found.

Then his mother said to him, "My son, it is certain that the slipper you found belongs to none other than the great mountain rajah's daughter; therefore take it to his palace, and when he offers you the promised reward say that you wish for neither silver nor gold, but ask him to give you his daughter in marriage. Thus you may gain her for your wife."

The prince did as his mother advised; and, when, after a long, long journey, he reached the court of Sodewa Bai's father, he presented the slipper to him, saying, "I have found your daughter's slipper, and for restoring it I claim a great reward." "What will you have?" said the rajah. "Shall I pay you in horses? or in silver? or gold?" "No," answered the prince, "I will have none of these things. I am the son of a rajah who lives in the plains, and I found this slipper in the jungle where I was hunting, and have traveled for many weary days to bring it you; but the only payment I care for is the hand of your beautiful daughter. If it pleases you, let me become your son-in-law." The rajah replied, "This only I cannot promise you; for I have vowed I will not oblige my daughter to marry against her will. This matter depends upon her alone. If she is willing to be your wife, I also am willing; but it rests with her free choice."

Now it happened that Sodewa Bai had from her window

seen the prince coming up to the palace gate, and when she heard his errand, she said to her father, "I saw that prince, and I am willing to marry him."

So they were married with great pomp and splendor.

When, however, all the other rajahs, Sodewa Bai's suitors, heard of her choice, they were much astonished, as well as vexed, and said, "What can have made Sodewa Bai take a fancy to that young prince? He is not so wonderfully hand-some, and he is very poor. This is a most foolish marriage." But they all came to it and were entertained at the palace, where the festivities lasted many days.

After Sodewa Bai and her husband had lived there for some little time, he one day said to his father-in-law, "I have a great desire to see my own people again, and to return to my own country. Let me take my wife home with me." The rajah said, "Very well. I am willing that you should go. Take care of your wife; guard her as the apple of your eye; and be sure you never permit the golden necklace to be taken from her neck and given to anyone else, for in that case she would die." The prince promised, and he returned with Sodewa Bai to his father's kingdom. At their departure the Rajah of the Moun-tain gave them many elephants, horses, camels and attendants, besides jewels innumerable and much money, and many rich hangings, robes and carpets.

The old Rajah and Ranee of the Plain were delighted to welcome home their son and his beautiful bride; and there they might all have lived their lives long in uninterrupted peace and happiness, had it not been for one unfortunate circum-stance. Rowjee (for that was the prince's name) had another wife, to whom he had been married when a child, long before he found Sodewa Bai's golden slipper. She, therefore, was the first ranee, though Sodewa Bai was the one he loved the best (for the first ranee was of a sullen, morose and jealous disposition). His father also, and his mother, preferred Sodewa Bai to their other daughter-in-law. The first ranee could not bear to think of anyone being ranee besides herself; and more especially of another not only in the same position but better loved by all around than she. Therefore, in her wicked heart she hated Sodewa Bai and longed for her destruction, though outwardly pretending to be very fond of her.

The old rajah and ranee, knowing the first ranee's jealous and envious disposition, never liked Sodewa Bai to be much with her; but as they had only a vague fear and no certain ground for alarm, they could do no more than watch both carefully; and Sodewa Bai, who was guileless and unsuspicious, would remonstrate with them when they warned her not to be so intimate with Rowjee Rajah's other wife, saying, "I have no fear. I think she loves me as I love her. Why should we disagree? Are we not sisters?"

One day Rowjee Rajah was obliged to go on a journey to a distant part of his father's kingdom, and being unable to take Sodewa Bai with him, he left her in his parents' charge, promising to return soon and begging them to watch over her, and to go every morning and see that she was well; which they agreed to do.

A little while after their husband had gone, the first ranee went to Sodewa Bai's room and said to her, "It is lonely for us both now Rowjee is away; but you must come often to see me, and I will come often to see you and talk to you, and so we will amuse ourselves as well as we can." To this Sodewa Bai agreed, and to amuse the first ranee she took out all her jewels and pretty things to show her. As they were looking over them, the first ranee said, "I notice you always wear that row of golden beads around your neck. Why do you? Have you any reason for always wearing the same ones?"

"Oh yes," answered Sodewa Bai thoughtlessly. "I was born with these beads round my neck, and the wise men told my father and mother that they contain my soul, and that if any-one else wore them I should die. So I always wear them. I have never once taken them off."

When the first ranee heard this news, she was very pleased. She feared to steal the beads herself because she was afraid she might be found out and because she did not like with her own hands to commit a crime. So, returning to her house, she called her most confidential servant, a Negress, whom she knew to be trustworthy, and said to her, "Go this evening to Sodewa Bai's room when she is asleep and take from her neck the string of golden beads, fasten them round your own neck and return to me. Those beads contain her soul, and as soon as you put them on she will cease to live." The Negress agreed to do as she was told; for she had long known that her mistress hated Sodewa Bai and desired nothing so much as her death. So that night, going softly into the sleeping ranee's room, she stole the golden necklace, and fastening it round her own neck, crept away without anyone knowing what she had done. And when the Negress put on the necklace, Sodewa Bai's spirit fled.

Next morning the old rajah and ranee went as usual to see their daughter-in-law and knocked at the door of her room. No one answered. They knocked again and again; still no reply. They then went in and found her lying there, cold as marble and quite dead, though she had seemed very well when they saw her only the day before. They asked her attendants, who slept just outside her door, whether she had been ill that night, or if anyone had gone into her room. But they declared they had heard no sound and were sure no one had been near the place. In vain the rajah and ranee sent for the most learned doctors in the kingdom to see if there was still any spark of life remaining. All said that the young ranee was dead, beyond reach of hope or help.

Then the rajah and ranee were very grieved, and mourned bitterly; and, because they desired that, if possible, Rowjee Rajah should see his wife once again, instead of burying her underground, they placed her beneath a canopy in a beautiful tomb near a little tank, and would go daily to vist the place and look at her. Then did a wonder take place such as had never been known throughout the land before! Sodewa Bai's body did not decay, nor the color of her face change. And a month afterwards, when her husband returned home, she looked as fair and lovely as on the night on which she died. There was a fresh color in her cheeks and on her lips; she seemed to be only asleep.

When poor Rowjee Rajah heard of her death, he was so brokenhearted they thought he also would die. He cursed the evil fate that had deprived him of hearing her last words, or bidding her farewell, if he could not save her life. And from morning to evening he would go to her tomb and rend the air with his passionate lamentations, and, looking through the grating to where she lay calm and still under the canopy, say, before he went away, "I will take one last look at that fair face. Tomorrow Death may have set his seal upon it. O loveliness too bright for earth! O lost, lost wife!" The rajah and ranee feared that he would die or go mad, and they tried to prevent his going to the tomb; but all was of no avail. It seemed to be the only thing he cared for in life.

Now the Negress who had stolen Sodewa Bai's necklace used to wear it all day long, but late each night on going to bed she would take it off and put it by till next morning, and, whenever she took it off, Sodewa Bai's spirit returned to her again and she lived till day dawned and the Negress put on the necklace, when she again died. But as the tomb was far from any houses and the old rajah and ranee and Rowjee Rajah only went there by day, nobody found this out.

When Sodewa Bai first came to life in this way, she felt very frightened to find herself there all alone in the dark, and thought she was in prison; but afterwards she got more accustomed to it and determined when morning came to look about the place and find her way back to the palace, and recover the necklace she found she had lost. It would have been dangerous to go at night through the jungles that surrounded the tomb, where she could hear the wild beasts roaring all night long. But morning never came, for whenever the Negress awoke and put on the golden beads, Sodewa Bai died.

However, each night when the ranee came to life, she would walk to the little tank by the tomb and drink some of the cool water and return; but food she had none. Now no pearls or precious stones fell from her lips, because she had no one to talk to; but each time she walked down to the tank she scattered jewels on either side of her path. One day when Rowjee Rajah went to the tomb, he noticed all these jewels, and, thinking it very strange (though he never dreamed that his wife could come to life), determined to watch and see whence they came. But although he watched and waited long, he could not find out the cause, because all day Sodewa Bai lay still and dead and only came to life at night.

It was just at this time, two whole months after she had been buried, and the night after the very day that Rowjee Rajah had spent in watching by the tomb, that Sodewa Bai had a little son. Directly after he was born, day dawned, and the mother died. The little lonely baby began to cry, but no one was there to hear him; and, as it chanced, the rajah did not go to the tomb that day, for he thought, "All yesterday I watched by the tomb and saw nothing; instead, therefore, of going today I will wait till the evening and then see again if I cannot find out how the jewels came there."

So at night he went to the place. When he got there he heard a faint cry from inside the tomb; but what it was he knew not. Perhaps it might be a peri or an evil spirit. As he was wondering, the door opened and Sodewa Bai crossed the courtyard to the tank with a child in her arms, and as she walked showers of jewels fell on both sides of her path. Rowjee Rajah thought he must be in a dream; but when he saw the ranee drink some water from the tank and return towards the tomb, he sprang up and hurried after her.

Sodewa Bai, hearing footsteps follow her, was frightened, and running into the tomb fastened the door. Then the rajah knocked at it, saying, "Let me in; let me in." She answered, "Who are you? Are you a rakshasa or a spirit?" For she thought that perhaps this was some cruel creature who would kill her and the child. "No, no," cried the rajah, "I am no rakshasa, but your husband. Let me in, Sodewa Bai, if you are indeed alive." No sooner did he name her name than she knew his voice, and unbolted the door and let him in. Then when he saw her sitting on the tomb with the baby on her lap, he fell down on his knees before her, saying, "Tell me, little wife, that this is not a dream." "No," she answered, "I am indeed alive, and this our child was born last night. But every day I die; for while you were away someone stole my golden neck-lace."

Then for the first time Rowjee Rajah noticed that the beads were no longer round her neck. So he bade her fear nothing, for that he would assuredly recover them and return; and going back to the palace, which he reached in the early morn-ing, he summoned before him the whole household.

Then, upon the neck of the Negress, servant to the first ranee, he saw Sodewa Bai's missing necklace, and, seizing it, ordered his guards to take the woman to prison. The Negress, frightened, confessed that all she had done was by the first ranee's order, and how, at her command, she had stolen the necklace. And when the rajah learnt this, he ordered that the first ranee also should be imprisoned for life. He and his father and mother all went together to the tomb, and, placing the lost beads round Sodewa Bai's neck, brought her and the child back in triumph with them to the palace. Then, at news of how the young ranee had been restored to life, there was great joy throughout all that country, and many days were spent in rejoicings in honor of that happy event. And for the rest of their lives the old rajah and ranee, and Rowjee Rajah and Sodewa Bai, and all the family, lived in health and happiness.

⋘⋙⋘⋙

33. Samson and His Woman

ONE DAY the Apostle (peace on him!) was expounding a chapter in the Koran when he came to the story of the Mes-senger Samson. Quoth the Apostle (peace on him!), "They say that Samson was a Messenger who warred for a thousand months in the cause of God Most High. He had his dwelling in a high hill; and in the daytime he would come down from the hill and war, and when it was evening he would return to the hill and sleep beside his wife. The misbelievers were power-less against Samson; and they agreed among themselves, say-ing, 'Let us give money to his wife that she may bind him and deliver him to us.' So they took a dish filled with gold and went to his wife and said 'Bind thy husband with this rope and deliver him to us, and this dish with the gold therein shall be thine.'

"When the woman saw so much money, she coveted it and said, 'So be it'; and she took the rope. Samson came back from fighting; and he was weary, and he lay down and slept. And the woman came and bound fast his hands with the rope. And she said to herself, 'This man is a Messenger, belike he may break this rope.' And wishing to try if it were so, she wakened Samson. He, seeing that his hands were bound, said, 'Who bound my hands?' His wife answered, 'I bound them; but what matter? Thou art a Messenger, pull and break the rope.' So Samson put forth his strength and strained and strained, and the rope broke. And he lay down again and slept. And the woman went and said to the misbelievers, 'He has broken the rope.'

"So they gave her chains, and again she bound him and wakened him to try him. Samson saw that his hands were bound again, and he said, 'Who has bound me?' She replied, 'I bound thee to try thee.' Samson again put forth his strength, and the chains were broken in pieces.

"And the woman was amazed, and said, 'O Prophet of

God, with what must one bind thee?' Samson answered, 'Nought but thy hair can avail.'

"Now the woman had two tresses of hair. These she cut off and bound round his hands, and then awakened him again. Samson saw that his hands were bound and he said, 'Who has bound me again?' The woman answered, 'She who has ever bound thee has bound thee; pull, strain.' Then she let these misbelievers, who were lying hidden, know; and they came forth and seized Samson and bare him to their city.

"And they cut off his two hands and his two feet and left him in a certain place and went away. And Samson (peace on him!) said, 'My God, give me again my hands and my feet that I may war in Thy cause.' Then Gabriel (peace on him!) came and touched him with his wing, and Samson was made whole again.

"The palace of their king was supported by a single column; and that palace was filled full of misbelievers. And Samson went and pulled down that column, and the palace fell to the ground, and as many disbelievers as were therein were killed. And Samson began again to war, and he ceased not from warring until that he was martyred."

❧⁓❧⁓

34. The Stealing of the Heart

MANY, MANY YEARS ago there ruled over a certain kingdom a chan named Guguluktschi. Upon the death of this chan his son, who was of great reputation and worth, was elected chan in his place.

One berren (a measure of distance) from the residence of the chan dwelt a man who had a daughter of wonderful abilities and extraordinary beauty. The son of the chan was enamored of this maiden and visited her daily, until at length he fell sick of a grievous malady and died, without the maiden being made aware of it.

One night just as the moon was rising the maiden heard a knocking at the door, and the face of the maiden was gladdened when she beheld the son of the chan. And the maiden arose and went to meet him, and she led him in and placed arrack and cakes before him. "Wife," said the son of the chan, "come with me!"

The maiden followed, and they kept going further and further until they arrived at the dwelling of the chan, from which proceeded the sound of cymbals and kettledrums.

"Chan, what is this?" she asked. The son of the chan replied to this inquiry of the maiden, "Do you not know that they are now celebrating the feast of my funeral?" Thus spake he; and the maiden exclaimed, "The feast of thy funeral! Has anything befallen the chan's son?"

And the son of the chan replied, "He is departed. Thou wilt, however, bear a son unto him. And when the season is come, go into the stable of the elephants and let him be born there. In the palace there will arise a contention betwixt my mother and her attendants because of the wonderful stone of the kingdom. The wonderful stone lies under the table of sacrifice. After it has been discovered, do you and my mother reign over this kingdom until such time as my son comes of age."

Thus spake he and vanished into air. But his beloved fell from very anguish into a swoon. "Chan! chan!" exclaimed she sorrowfully when she came to herself again. And because she felt that the time was come, she betook herself to the stable of the elephants and there gave birth to a son.

On the following morning when the keeper of the elephants entered the stable, he exclaimed, "What! has a woman given birth to a son in the stable of the elephants? This never happened before. This may be an injury to the elephants."

At these words the maiden said, "Go unto the mother of the chan and say unto her, 'Arise! something wonderful has taken place.'"

When these words were told unto the mother of the chan, she arose and went unto the stable, and the maiden related unto her all that had happened. "Wonderful!" said the mother of the chan. "Otherwise the chan had left no successors. Let us go together into the house."

Thus speaking, she took the maiden with her into the house. And she nursed her and tended her carefully. Because her account of the wonderful stone was found to be correct, all the rest of her story was believed. So the mother of the chan and his wife ruled over the kingdom.

Henceforth, too, it happened that every month on the night of the full moon the deceased chan appeared to his wife, remained with her until morning dawned, and then vanished into air. And the wife recounted this to his mother, but his mother believed her not and said, "This is a mere invention. If it were true, my son, of a surety, would show himself likewise unto me. If I am to believe your words, you must take care that mother and son meet one another."

When the son of the chan came on the night of the full

moon, his wife said unto him, "It is well that thou comest unto me on the night of every full moon, but it were yet better if thou camest every night." And as she spake thus, with tears in her eyes, the son of the chan replied, "If thou hadst sufficient spirit to dare its accomplishment, thou mightest do what would bring me every night; but thou art young and cannot do it." "Then," said she, "if thou wilt but come every night, I will do all that is required of me, although I should thereby lose both flesh and bone."

Thereupon the son of the chan spake as follows: "Then betake thyself on the night of the full moon a berren from this place to the iron old man and give unto him arrack. A little further you will come unto two rams; to them you must offer batschimak cakes. A little further on you will perceive a host of men in coats of mail and other armor, and there you must share out meat and cakes. From thence you must proceed to a large black building, stained with blood. The skin of a man floats over it instead of a flag. Two fiends stand at the entrance. Present unto them both offerings of blood. Within the mansion thou wilt discover nine fearful exorcists and nine hearts upon a throne. 'Take me! take me!' will the eight old hearts exclaim; and the ninth heart will cry out, 'Do not take me!' But leave the old hearts and take the fresh one, and run home with it without looking round."

Much as the maiden was alarmed at the task which she had been enjoined to perform, she set forth on the night of the next full moon, divided the offerings and entered the house. "Take me not!" exclaimed the fresh heart; but the maiden seized the fresh heart and fled with it. The exorcists pursued her and cried out to those who were watching, "Stop the thief of the heart!" And the two fiends cried, "We have received offerings of blood!" Then each of the armed men cried out, "Stop the thief!" But the rams said, "We have received batschimak cakes." Then they called out to the iron old man, "Stop the thief with the heart!" But the old man said, "I have received arrack from her and shall not stop her."

Thereupon the maiden journeyed on without fear until she reached home. And she found upon entering the house the chan's son, attired in festive garments. And the chan's son drew nigh and threw his arms about the neck of the maiden.

◈◈◈

35. *La Donna Mobile*

THERE WAS ONCE a tailor youth who had a fair wife, and they greatly loved one another. One day they made a pact that if the woman died first, the husband should take no other wife, but throw his arms round her tombstone and weep till morning. And, if the youth died first, the woman should do likewise. By the decree of God the woman died. After the tailor had wept and lamented he buried her and fulfilled his pact, and threw his arms round his wife's tombstone and wept. And he constantly kept watch over the grave. One day Jesus (peace on him!), when passing by that place, saw a youth weeping and embracing a tombstone, and he went up to him and asked why he wept. The youth related all. Then Jesus (peace on him!) prayed, and the woman became alive and came forth from the grave in her shroud. And Jesus (peace on him!) proceeded on his way.

The youth said, "One cannot go thus in a shroud; wait thou here a moment till I go fetch clothes from the house. Then thou shalt put on those clothes, and we will go together." And he went quickly to the house, leaving the woman there.

Suddenly the son of the king of that country passed that spot and saw a fair woman sitting wrapped in a shroud. As soon as the prince saw that woman, he fell in love with her from heart and soul, and he said to her, "Who art thou?" She answered, "I am a stranger; a robber has stripped me." Thereupon the prince ordered his servants to take the woman to the palace and clothe her in clean garments.

When the youth returned with the clothes he found not the woman there, and he cried and asked of the passers-by. No one had seen her. The poor man, asking and asking, met the prince's servants. These asked the tailor why he wept. He replied, "For a time my wife was dead; but now, praise be to God, she is become alive through the prayer of the Messenger Jesus. I went to fetch her clothes, but she has disappeared. Therefore do I weep." They answered, "The prince sent that lady to the palace this day."

Thereupon the tailor went before the prince and complained, saying, "The woman thou hast taken is my wife." The prince asked the lady; she denied and said, "This is the robber who stripped me of my clothes and made off. Praise be to God; if thou kill him now, thou shalt gain great reward." The prince commanded that they bind both the tailor's hands behind his back. Although the poor tailor cried aloud, it was no avail. They put a rope round his neck and led him to the gallows. Then they perceived St. Jesus on the road, and they waited. When he came near he asked of their case, and they told him. Then he bade them stop and went himself to the prince. They called the woman, and he said, "This woman is the wife of yonder youth; I prayed and she became alive." When the woman saw the Messenger she was unable to deny, but spake the truth. Jesus (peace on him!) prayed again, and that woman died; and the youth was rescued from the abyss whereinto he had fallen, and he repented of his having wept so long a time.

❧❦❧❦❧

36. *Hacon Grizzlebeard*

ONCE ON A TIME there was a princess who was so proud and pert that no suitor was good enough for her. She made game of them all and sent them about their business, one after the other. But, though she was so proud, still new suitors kept on coming to the palace, for she was a beauty, the wicked hussy!

So one day there came a prince to woo her, and his name was Hacon Grizzlebeard. The first night he was there the princess bade the king's fool cut off the ears of one of the prince's horses, and slit the jaws of the other up to the ears. When the prince went out to drive next day, the princess stood in the porch and looked at him.

"Well!" she cried, "I never saw the like of this in all my life. The keen north wind that blows here has taken the ears off one of your horses, and the other has stood by and gaped at what was going on till his jaws have split right up to his ears."

And with that she burst out into a roar of laughter, ran in, slammed to the door and let him drive off. So he drove home, but as he went he thought to himself that he would pay her off one day.

After a bit he put on a great beard of moss, threw a great fur cloak over his clothes and dressed himself up just like any beggar. He went to a goldsmith and bought a golden spinning wheel and sat down with it under the princess' window and began to file away at his spinning wheel, and to turn it this way and that, for it wasn't quite in order, and besides wanted a stand.

So when the princess rose up in the morning, she came to the window and threw it up and called out to the beggar if he would sell his golden spinning wheel. "No; it isn't for sale," said Hacon Grizzlebeard, "but if I may have leave to sleep outside your bedroom door tonight, I'll give it you." Well, the princess thought it a good bargain; there could be no danger in letting him sleep outside her door. So she got the wheel, and at night Hacon Grizzlebeard lay down outside her bedroom. But as the night wore on he began to freeze.

"Hutetutetutetu! it is *so* cold; do let me in," he cried.

"You've lost your wits outright, I think," said the princess.

"Oh, hutetutetutetu! it is so bitter cold, pray do let me in," said Hacon again.

"Hush! hush! hold your tongue!" said the princess. "If my father were to know that there was a man in the house, I should be in a fine scrape."

"Oh, hutetutetutetu! I'm almost frozen to death. Only let me come inside and lie on the floor."

Yes! There was no help for it. She had to let him in, and, when he was, he lay on the ground and slept like a top.

Some time after, Hacon came again with the stand to the spinning wheel and sat down under the princess' window and began to file at it, for it was not quite fit for use. When she heard him filing, she threw up the window and began to talk to him and to ask what he had there.

"Oh! only the stand to that spinning wheel which your royal highness bought; for I thought, as you had the wheel, you might like to have the stand too."

"What do you want for it?" asked the princess. But it was not for sale any more than the wheel, but she might have it if she would give him leave to sleep on the floor of her bedroom next night. Well! she gave him leave, only he was to be sure to lie still and not to shiver and call out "hutetu" or any such stuff. Hacon promised fair enough, but as the night wore on he began to shiver and shake, and to ask whether he might not come nearer and lie on the floor alongside the princess' bed. There was no help for it; she had to give him leave lest the king should hear the noise he made. So he lay alongside the princess' bed and slept like a top.

It was a long while before he came again, but when he came he had with him a golden wool winder, and he sat down and began to file away at it under the princess' window. Then came the old story over again. When the princess heard what was going on, she came to the window and asked him how he did and whether he would sell the golden wool winder. "It is not to be had for money; but if you will give me leave to sleep tonight in your bedroom with my head on your bedstead, you shall have it for nothing." Well! she would give him leave if he only gave his word to be quiet and make no noise. So he said he would do his best to be still; but as the night wore on he began to shiver and shake so that his teeth chattered again.

"Hutetutetutetu! it is so bitter cold! Oh, do let me get into bed and warm myself a little."

"Get into bed?" said the princess. "Why, you must have lost your wits." "Hutetutetutetu!" said Hacon. "Do let me get into bed. Hutetutetutetu!"

"Hush! hush! be still for God's sake," said the princess. "If father knows there is a man in here, I shall be in a sad plight. I'm sure he'll kill me on the spot."

"Hutetutetutetu! let me get into bed," said Hacon Grizzle-beard, who kept on shivering so that the whole room shook. Well! there was no help for it; she had to let him get into bed, where he slept both sound and soft. But three-quarters of a year later the princess had a child, at which the king grew so wild with rage that he was near making an end of both mother and babe.

Just after this happened came Hacon tramping that way once more, as if by chance, and took his seat down in the kitchen, like any other beggar. When the princess came and saw him, she cried, "Ah, God have mercy on me for the ill luck you have brought on me. Father is ready to burst with rage. Do let me follow you to your home."

"Oh! I'll be bound you're too well bred to follow me, for I have nothing but a log hut to live in. And how I shall ever get food for you I can't tell, for it's just as much as I can do to get food for myself."

"Oh yes! it's all the same to me how you get it, or whether you get it at all," she said, "only let me be with you, for if I stay here any longer my father will be sure to take my life."

So she got leave to be with the beggar, as she called him,

and they walked a long, long way, though she was but a poor hand at tramping. When she passed out of her father's land into another, she asked whose it was. "Oh! this is Hacon Grizzlebeard's, if you must know," said he. "Indeed!" said the princess. "I might have married him if I chose, and then I should not have had to walk about like a beggar's wife."

So, whenever they came to grand castles, and woods, and parks, and she asked whose they were, the beggar's answer was still the same: "Oh! they are Hacon Grizzlebeard's." And the princess was in a sad way that she had not chosen the man who had such broad lands. Last of all they came to a palace, where he said he was known, and where he thought he could get her work, so that they might have something to live on. So he built up a cabin by the woodside for them to dwell in. And every day he went to the king's palace, as he said, to hew wood and draw water for the cook, and when he came back he brought a few scraps of meat; but they did not go very far.

One day when he came home from the palace, he said, "To-morrow I will stay at home and look after the baby, but you must get ready to go to the palace, do you hear! for the prince said you were to come and try your hand at baking." "I bake!" said the princess. "I can't bake, for I never did such a thing in my life." "Well, you must go," said Hacon, "since the prince has said it. If you can't bake, you can learn. You have only got to look how the rest bake. And mind, when you leave, you must steal me some bread."

"I can't steal," said the princess.

"You can learn that too; you know we live but poorly. But take care that the prince doesn't see you, for he has eyes at the back of his head."

So when she was well on her way, Hacon ran by a short cut

and reached the palace long before her, and threw off his rags and beard and put on his princely robes. The princess took her turn in the bakehouse and did as Hacon bade her, for she stole bread till her pockets were crammed full. So when she was about to go home at even, the prince said, "We don't know whether this beggar's wife is honest or not; I think we'd best see if she has taken anything away with her." So he thrust his hand into all her pockets and felt her all over, and when he found the bread, he was in a great rage and led them all a sad life. She began to weep and bewail, and said, "The beggar made me do it, and I couldn't help it."

"Well," said the prince at last, "it ought to have gone hard with you, but all the same, for the sake of the beggar you shall be forgiven this once."

When she was well on her way, he threw off his robes, put on his skin cloak and his false beard, and reached the cabin before her. When she came home, he was busy nursing the baby. "Well, you have made me do what it went against my heart to do. This is the first time I ever stole, and this shall be the last." And with that she told him how it had gone with her, and what the prince had said.

A few days after, Hacon came home at even and said, "Tomorrow I must stay at home and mind the babe, for they are going to kill a pig at the palace and you must help to make the sausages."

"I make sausages!" said the princess. "I can't do any such thing. I have eaten sausages often enough; but as to making them, I never made one in my life."

Well, there was no help for it. The prince had said it and go she must. As for not knowing how, she was only to do what the others did, and at the same time Hacon bade her steal some sausages for him. "Nay, but I can't steal them," she said. "You know how it went last time." "Well, you can learn to steal; who knows but you may have better luck next time."

When she was well on her way, Hacon ran by a short cut, reached the palace long before her, threw off his skin cloak and false beard, and stood in the kitchen in his royal robes before she came in. So the princess stood by when the pig was killed and made sausages with the rest, and did as Hacon bade her, and stuffed her pockets full of sausages. But when she was about to go home at even, the prince said, "This beggar's wife was long-fingered last time; we may as well just see if she hasn't carried anything off." So he began to thrust his hands into her pockets. When he found the sausages, he was in a great rage again and made a great to-do, threatening to send for the constable and put her into a cage.

"Oh, God bless your royal highness; do let me off! The beggar made me do it," she said, and wept bitterly. "Well," said Hacon, "you ought to smart for it; but for the beggar's sake you shall be forgiven."

When she was gone, he changed his clothes again, ran by the short cut, and, when she reached the cabin, there he was before her. Then she told him the whole story, and swore, through thick and thin, it should be the last time he got her to do such a thing.

Now, it fell out a little time after, when the man came back from the palace, he said, "Our prince is going to be married, but the bride is sick, so the tailor can't measure her for her wedding gown. And the prince's will is that you should go up to the palace and be measured instead of the bride; for he says you are just the same height and shape. But after you have been measured, mind you, don't go away. You can stand about, you know, and, when the tailor cuts out the gown, you can snap up the largest pieces and bring them home for a waist-coat for me."

"Nay, but I can't steal," she said. "Besides, you know how it went last time." "You can learn then," said Hacon, "and you may have better luck, perhaps."

She thought it bad, but still she went and did as she was told. She stood by while the tailor was cutting out the gown, and she swept down all the biggest scraps and stuffed them into her pockets. When she was going away, the prince said, "We may as well see if this old girl has not been long-fingered this time too." So he began to feel and search her pockets, and when he found the pieces he was in a rage and began to stamp and scold at a great rate, while she wept and said, "Ah, pray forgive me. The beggar bade me do it, and I couldn't help it."

"Well, you ought to smart for it," said Hacon. "But for the beggar's sake it shall be forgiven you."

So it went now just as it had gone before, and when she got back to the cabin, the beggar was there before her. "Oh, heaven help me," she said. "You will be the death of me at last by making me nothing but what is wicked. The prince was in such a towering rage that he threatened me both with the constable and the cage."

Some time after Hacon came home to the cabin at even and said, "Now the prince's will is that you should go up to the palace and stand for the bride, old lass! for the bride is still sick and keeps her bed. But he won't put off the wedding. And he says you are so like her that no one could tell one from the other. So tomorrow you must get ready to go to the palace."

"I think you've lost your wits, both the prince and you," said she. "Do you think I look fit to stand in the bride's place? Look at me! Can any beggar's trull look worse than I?"

"Well, the prince said you were to go, and so go you must."

There was no help for it, go she must. And when she reached the palace, they dressed her out so finely that no princess ever looked so smart. The bridal train went to church, where she stood for the bride, and when they came back there was dancing and merriment in the palace. But just as she was in the midst of dancing with the prince, she saw a gleam of light through the window, and lo! the cabin by the woodside was all one bright flame.

"Oh! the beggar and the babe and the cabin," she screamed out, and was just going to swoon away.

"Here is the beggar and there is the babe, and so let the cabin burn away," said Hacon Grizzlebeard.

Then she knew him again, and after that the mirth and merriment began in right earnest. But since that I have never heard tell anything more about them.

❦❧❦❧

37. Beauty Treatment

THERE WAS ONCE a king who wanted to marry. But his wife must be more beautiful than the sun, and no matter how many maidens he saw, none was beautiful enough to suit him. Then he called his trusty servant and commanded him to seek everywhere and see whether he could find a beautiful girl. The servant set out and wandered through the whole land but found none who seemed handsome enough to him. One day, however, after he had run about a great deal and was very thirsty, he came to a little house. He knocked and asked for a drink of water. Now there dwelt in the house two very old women—one eighty and the other ninety years old—who supported themselves by spinning. When the servant asked for water, the one eighty years old rose, opened a little wicket in the shutter and handed him out the water. From spinning so much her hands were very white and delicate, and when the servant saw them he thought, "It must be a handsome maiden, for she has such a delicate white hand." So he hastened to the king and said, "Your royal majesty, I have found what you seek; so and so has happened to me." "Very well," answered the king. "Go once more and try to see her."

The servant returned to the little house, knocked and asked again for some water. The old woman did not open the window but handed him the pitcher through the little opening in the shutter. "Do you live here all alone?" asked the servant. "No," she answered. "I live here with my sister. We are poor girls and support ourselves by the work of our hands." "How old are you, then?" "I am fifteen and my sister twenty."

The servant went back to the king and told him all, and the king said, "I will take the one who is fifteen. Go and bring her to me." When the servant returned to the two old women and told them that the king wished to elevate the younger to the position of his wife, she answered, "Tell the king I am ready to do his will. Since my birth no ray of the sun has ever struck me, and if a ray of the sun or a beam of light should strike me now, I would become perfectly black. Ask the king, therefore, to send a closed carriage for me at night, and I will come to his palace."

When the king heard this he sent royal apparel and a closed carriage, and at night the old woman covered her face with a thick veil and rode to the palace. The king received her joyfully and begged her to lay aside the veil. She replied, "There are too many lighted candles here; their light would make me black." So the king married her without having seen her face. When they came into the king's chamber, however, and she removed her veil, the king saw for the first time what an ugly old woman he had married, and in his rage he opened the window and threw her out.

Fortunately, there was a spike in the wall, on which she caught by her clothes and remained hanging between heaven and earth. Four fairies chanced to pass by, and when they saw the old woman hanging there, one of them cried, "See, sisters, there is the old woman who cheated the king. Shall we wish her dress to tear and let her fall?" "Oh, no! let us not do that," cried the youngest and most beautiful of the fairies. "Let us rather wish her something good. I wish her youth." "And I, beauty." "And I, prudence." "And I, a good heart." Thus the fairies cried, and while they were yet speaking the old woman became a wondrous fair maiden.

The next morning when the king looked out of the window and saw the beautiful girl hanging there, he was terrified, and thought, "Unhappy man! What have I done! Had I no eyes last night?" Then he had her carefully taken down with long ladders and begged her pardon, saying, "Now we will have a great festival and be right happy." So they celebrated a splendid feast, and the young queen was the fairest in the whole city.

But one day the sister ninety years old came to the palace to visit the queen, her sister. "Who is this ugly creature?" asked the king. "An old neighbor of mine who is half-witted," replied the queen quickly.

The old woman kept looking at her rejuvenated sister and asked, "What did you do to become so young and lovely? I too would like to be young and pretty again." She kept asking this the whole day, until the queen finally lost her patience and said, "I had my old skin taken off, and this new, smooth skin came to light."

The old woman went to a barber-surgeon and said, "I will give you what you will to remove my old skin, so that I may become young and handsome again." "But, good old woman, you will surely die if I skin you." The old woman would not listen to him, and at last he had to do her will. He took his knife and made a cut in her forehead. "Oh!" cried the old woman.

> "Who will look fair
> Must grief and pain bear,"

answered the barber. "Then skin away, master," said the old woman. The barber kept cutting on until all at once the old woman fell down dead.

38. *The Devil Tries Marriage*

ONE DAY ages ago, gracious ladies, the Devil declared that he was fed up with stories men told about the miseries of matrimony. Perhaps, the demon thought, these mortals do not employ any more imagination in the management of their marital affairs than they do in their monotonous recitals of their marital troubles. Doubtless he could conduct the business better. He decided to marry himself and see. So he took the name of Pancrace Stornel and the form of a handsome well-bred young man. Soon the rumor that he was fabulously wealthy spread through the town. Consequently, a great many pretty ladies in the marriage market saw to it that he met them. One of these, Sylvia Balastro by name, struck his fancy, and he chose her to be his mate.

No lady, no matter how fond of pomp and circumstance, would have been disappointed with anything having to do with either the marriage feast or the ceremony. No money was spared; everything was magnificent. However, the *compare* or best man, Casper Boncy, was by profession only a sharper or rook.

"Sylvia, my dear wife, whom I love more than my life," said the Devil a few days after the marriage, "you now have had many proofs of my love. By doing something that would be easy for you and very pleasing to me, you could prove that you are fond of me. It is to make a list of all the wearing apparel, jewels, and all the feminine trappings you need or want now, or will need or want in the years to come. When you hand me the list, I will purchase everything in it for you if you will promise me never to bother me again with requests for such things. Will you accept this proposal?"

Sylvia asked for time, for she wished to talk it over with her mother, a woman as rusé and knowing as her daughter. She listened to what the Devil had proposed. Then she called for pen and ink and wrote down a list as long as ten well ropes. Handing it to Sylvia, she said, "Tell your husband you will be fully satisfied with him if he will buy these for you."

"Are you certain that everything you want or will want is down here?" asked the Devil after he had run his eye down the catalogue of items. As Sylvia couldn't think of anything else to ask for, she told him she was absolutely certain. "And," she added, "I promise never, never to ask for anything more." "Good," said her spouse, "for neither sighs, prayers nor tears will ever get you more."

The house could scarcely hold all those things. Sylvia was the most glorious, the best dressed and bejeweled lady in the whole town. She was mad with joy.

A month later there was to be a magnificent feast in the town. All of the most elegant and prominent ladies were going to it. Of course Sylvia was invited. But, alas, the ladies just then decided to change the fashions, and they were all going to wear gowns of the new mode. When Sylvia got word of this, she realized that she was in a nice pickle. Nothing in her wardrobes would do; everything was hopelessly passé. So she fell into a deep melancholy. She was so cast down and vexed that all she could do at night was to toss and turn. The Devil discovered then that it was more difficult to sleep with a fretful woman than in a bed full of fleas. Sighs and moans issued from the depths of the poor woman's being.

Her bedfellow knew full well what the matter was. "What is it, Sylvia?" he asked. "Why are you so put out? Don't you want to go to the feast?" As these questions seemed to her to spring from sympathetic interest, she roused up her courage and said, "How can you wish, my dear husband, that I be seen at the feast when all I have to wear are some antiquated frocks? Could you have forgotten the old proverb: As good be out of the world as out of fashion? Nothing I have is at all like what the other ladies will be wearing. I am sure they will make fun of me."

"Well, Sylvia," said he, "although I have kept my part of the bargain, I see that you do not mean to keep yours. However, this once I will provide all the new-fangled dresses you think necessary to make a fine showing at the feast. But I warn you, if you break your promise again, you will be very sorry."

Now a few months later the styles changed again. This greatly vexed Sylvia, but she was afraid to let her husband see that it did. After a while the Devil, perceiving her melancholy and easily guessing the cause of it, said to her, "What is it, my love, that makes you so cast down?" As his voice was kind, she took heart and said, "I think I have reason to be sad and vexed, for I have no dresses that are in style. I couldn't bear to appear in public in my ancient frocks. The other ladies would point their fingers at me and laugh, and that would bring us into great discredit. Considering my steadfast faithfulness and humble obedience to you as my dear husband, do you believe I merit such a shameful and scandalous disgrace?"

"Are you blaming me for this state of your affairs?" asked the Devil. "Do not forget that twice I have provided everything you asked for! Brimstone and bouncing thunder! What a great lie it would be if I said that I understood you. However, for the third time I will order the apparel you want, but by the time you bedizen yourself with it I will be so far away you will never get tidings of me." So the Devil left Sylvia, and without one word of farewell.

He went to Amalfi and entered the body of the duke and tormented him sorely. Now it happened just at this time that

Casper Boncy, the sharper who had been the Devil's *compare*, arrived in Amalfi. He had preferred leaving his town to taking up residence in jail, some of his pretty card tricks having been detected. But his luck was still down on him in Amalfi; he was caught red-handed cheating at hazard. One gentleman was so angry with him that he vowed to get revenge. He thought of a way. He went straight to the Duke of Amalfi and told him he had found a man who claimed he could cast out demons. Now to the ears of the duke, who had been having a sad time with his demon and had not been able to find any-one able to cast him out, these words were like music. He instantly sent for the sharper. It was in vain that the poor sharper denied ever having said he could cast out devils and insisted that he knew nothing about the business, for he was not believed. "Either you cast out my demon and get a château of mine as reward," said the duke, "or be hanged and strangled between the columns of my castle."

These words threw a terrible fright into Boncy. He ran to his lodgings and tried to recall some of the things he had heard at various times about demons and how to oust them. He could remember a few of the things to do, but not clearly. Nevertheless, he decided to try some of them since anything was better than nothing.

Returning to the duke's palace, he ordered servants to hang St.-John's-wort and rue in the corners of the duke's chamber, to filch some holy water and sprinkle it about, and to burn incense and sulphur. Then he put down a pallet in the middle of the room and laid the duke upon it. Next he attempted to persuade the evil spirit to come out by flattery and sweet words. Then he tried to scare him out with threats and scurrilous language. None of all this had the least effect, and the duke became impatient.

The sharper was nonplused. Then he realized that he had forgotten to do what everyone had said was the most important thing of all—get the demon's name! Fortunately for Boncy the Devil himself now lent a helping hand. "My *compare*," said the Devil, "it is cruel and wicked of you to try to oust me from this most comfortable lodging."

So the demon knew him! "Zooks, sirs," cried the sharper in amazement. "I am beginning to believe that once upon a time I was best man to the Devil!"

"Go away, Boncy," cried the Devil, "and do not bother me further." "Pancrace Stornel," said the sharper, "first do me a favor—leave the duke. On the strength of the tie which binds bridegroom and *compare* I beg it of you. If you refuse, I will be hanged high between the columns of this palace."

"All the world knows such a tie is not worth a nutshell," said the demon. "As for you, my *compare*, I wish nothing more than to see you hanged high and then plunged into the deepest abyss of hell!" "What made you leave your wife?" asked the sharper. "That is none of your business," answered the evil spirit, with an oath. Could it be, thought the other, that the Devil, just like other husbands, feared his wife? Why, certainly; it could not be otherwise.

"Seignior Duke," cried Boncy, "you may now rejoice, for tomorrow morning at eleven your demon will be cast out! Just at eleven have all the musicians come to your palace and play loudly on their instruments. Order all the sextons to ring the church bells and all the cannoneers to fire their cannons. In this way we will celebrate your deliverance from the demon."

The next morning at eleven Boncy was busy conjuring the demon when suddenly there was a tremendous uproar—church bells rang, cannons roared, horns blared and drums boomed. It seemed that the end of the world had come. The Devil was startled. "Pray tell me, Boncy," he cried, "what is this terrible din?"

"My diabolical friend, hear this," said the sharper. "The duke has been informed that for reasons best known to you, you abandoned and fled from your wife, and he guessed that possibly she might want to see you again. Since you have turned a deaf ear to our kind invitations to leave, he thought you might listen to her. Thus he dared hope to reap some benefit from her presence here. So he sent someone to fetch her. The great hubbub you hear is to celebrate her arrival."

This news threw a great fright into the demon. "O wicked *compare*," cried he in an anguished voice, "you are more cunning than I. It is you who have invented this sly scheme. The mere thought of my wife fills me with hate, loathing, and horror. Why, I'd rather dwell in the deepest caverns of hell than have her at my side again. I wish to leave this place instantly and go far, far away."

With these words Pancrace Stornel left the body of the duke and vanished, leaving a terrible stench behind. After a few days the duke recovered his former vigor and well-being, and he gave Boncy a fine château. But Madame Sylvia, discovering one day that all her dresses and jewels had turned into ashes, died of a broken heart.

39. *The Laird of Balmachie's Wife*

IN THE OLDEN TIMES when it was the fashion for gentlemen to wear swords, the Laird of Balmachie went one day to
Dundee, leaving his wife at home ill in bed. Riding home in
the twilight, he had occasion to leave the high road, and
when crossing between some little romantic knolls, called
the Cur-hills, in the neighborhood of Carlungy, he encountered a troop of fairies supporting a kind of litter, upon
which some person seemed to be borne. Being a man of daunt-
less courage, and, as he said, impelled by some internal im-
pulse, he pushed his horse close to the litter, drew his sword,
laid it across the vehicle and in a firm voice exclaimed, "In
the name of God, release your captive."

The tiny troop immediately disappeared, dropping the litter
on the ground. The laird dismounted and found that it con-
tained his own wife, dressed in her bedclothes. Wrapping his
coat around her, he placed her on the horse before him, and
having only a short distance to ride, arrived safely home.

Placing her in another room under the care of an attentive
friend, he immediately went to the chamber where he had
left his wife in the morning, and there to all appearance she
still lay, very sick of a fever. She was fretful, discontented,
and complained much of having been neglected in his
absence, at all of which the laird affected great concern, and,
pretending much sympathy, insisted upon her rising to have

her bed made. She said that she was unable to rise, but her husband was peremptory, and, having ordered a large wood fire to warm the room, he lifted the imposter from the bed, and, bearing her across the floor as if to a chair, which had been previously prepared, he threw her on the fire, from which she bounced like a skyrocket and went through the ceiling and out at the roof of the house, leaving a hole among the slates.

He then brought in his own wife, a little recovered from her alarm. She said that sometime after sunset, the nurse having left her for the purpose of preparing a little caudle, a multitude of elves came in at the window, thronging like bees from a hive. They filled the room, and, having lifted her from the bed, carried her through the window, after which she recollected nothing further till she saw her husband standing over her on the Cur-hills, at the back of Carlungy. The hole in the roof, by which the female fairy made her escape, was mended, but could never be kept in repair, as a tempest of wind happened always once a year, which uncovered that particular spot, without injuring any other part of the roof.

❧❧❧❧

40. *The O'Donoghue in the Lake*

IN THE OLD TIMES—God be wid them!—before the Sassenach had conquered the Milesian or the invader had stepped upon our beautiful coast, lived O'Donoghue, a brave and mighty prince, in these parts of Lough Lane. He was as fine and as portly a man as a body could see in a day's walk; and 'twould do one's heart good to see him handle a hurdly and play at goal. Shure to see him leap and run, and hunt, and course, and swim, as I'm tould, there was no man, at all at all, could come near him, so that 'twas given up to him to be the finest and bravest *bouhel* that was ever created. Ross Castle belonged to him and, of course, all the estates about, and rat the better master never heard a poor man's complaint. He was noways hard on the poor people, and if they couldn't pay, he wouldn't be dhriving and canting all the beasts they had in the world the very minit the gale became due. So the blessings of every cabin were always praying for every luck for him and his.

Besides all this he knew a power that no person ever else guessed of. He was larned in every sort of books, an', in short, there was nothin' but he could do. But he sould himself, as they say, to the ould boy, and, by his manes, he was able to change himself into any shape or form that he plased. To be shure, 'twas a great gift, but it ill became so fine a gintleman to think so little of his soul.

As I say, he sould himself; but the bargin was, that if a woman should screech while he was in the enchantment, he should give himself up to him; and well, you may be shure that for a long time O'Donoghue took very good care that there was no woman by whenever he diverted his friends by changing his appearance into whatever shapes they would be calling after. However, his fame went about increasing wonderfully, and he was the talk of every place, while there was not a spalpeen in the whole country that did not wonder at all that he used to do.

He was goen on this way, as you may say, for some years, livin' in fine style and havin' the lade among all the princes round about, when, at last, it happened that his wife—an' 'twas she that was as fair an' as nate a colheen as any other in the whole world—says to him, "O'Donoghue, avourneen! why don't you ever show me any of your meracles that there's such talks about? Shure I could do no harm at all, an' one would think that you'd gratify your own wife before any stranger," says she.

And she went on pressing him afther sich a manner that he couldn't find it in his heart to refuse her yellow locks an' her large light eyes anything at all that she'd be after axing.

"Well, then," says he, "Aileen, dear, you mustn't open your mouth, nor say a single word, whatever becomes of me," says he; "or if you do, all is lost."

An' so she promised to be very quiet, an' to be frighted noways at all, an' to do whatever he tould her. Then, why, as well became him, O'Donoghue made himself into an elegant stag, an' kept leaping and running about the coort for a time, delighting all that was lookin' on. When he grew tired of that, he became the most beautifullest fish that ever you saw, an' no one knew how or what way he changed himself. Makin' a sort of a kind of a pool on the tiptop of the castle, he began swimming there, an' the castle began to go round, round, and topsy-turvy, like a whirligig. When his lady saw the danger, she got quite beside herself, an' forgettin' all his commands, she gave a terrible screech, through the mere fright of her. An' shure enough for 'im a sore screech 'twas for her, for the ould fellow, without another word, took a leap into the lake, an' was never seen alive from that day to this.

Notes

1. "The Scar" is from *Contes et Légendes du Caucase*, 1888, by J. Mourier. The editor's translation. An Armenian tale. In folktales it is foolish to suppose one can escape his destiny or the fulfillment of a prophecy. A close parallel of our story was current in eighteenth-century England as a ballad entitled "The Stepney Lady."

2. "The Goat-Girl" is from *Folklore of Modern Greece*, 1884, by Edmund M. Geldart. There is a touch of Cinderella in this story of an animal bride. In folktales, as with many a modern fashionable lady, the outer covering is of great importance. If a person puts on a swan skin he becomes a swan; or if he gets into a wolf's skin (with the proper incantation) he becomes a werewolf. Often there is a magic sympathetic tie between the covering and its wearer even though separated. For example, if a werewolf's skin is placed in a hot oven, the owner of the skin, no matter how far away, will suffer from the heat. The burning of a magic skin usually causes great pain to its owner, and it always ends the possibility of transformation. For a painless burning see No. 144 in Grimms' *Household Tales*.

3. "King O'Hara's Daughters" is from *Myths and Folklore of Ireland*, 1889, by Jeremiah Curtin. This tale belongs to one of the most widely dispersed and important folktale types, that of Cupid and Psyche. It is quite likely that the archetype tells of a celestial being who is condemned to live on earth and take on the form of an animal during the day. When night comes he can lay aside the bestial husk and become his real, radiantly handsome self again. In many versions the animal form is due to a spell cast by a witch. To question the fairy wife about her origin is taboo; the woman who loves the shape-changing hero must not reveal his double nature to anyone. But she violates this or another taboo, or disobeys him, and he disappears. She sets out in search of him and undergoes great hard-

ships. However, at last she finds him and the spell which has been cast over him is taken off, or the term of his punishment comes to an end, and the lovers are happily reunited.

Tales of this type often conclude with the motif of the Forgotten Fiancée or Supplanted Bride, as does our story. However, our hero does not avoid drinking the sleeping potion the third night, as is usual in these stories. Our tale also differs in that all three sisters marry husbands that change shape, the wife is able to accompany her husband until he marries the bad queen, and this woman has a separable soul and must be slain in the manner made use of when the creature to be killed is a giant who for safety has hidden his soul (strength, heart) in an egg or similar secret place. The cloak of darkness, a wishing cloak here, is usually a cloak of invisibility.

4. "Absent Without Leave" is from *Popular Tales of the West Highlands*, 1860, by J. F. Campbell, where it is called "The Three Soldiers." Slightly shortened. In some versions the three great red girls are swan maidens. In our tale the magic tablecloth can not only produce food but transport persons to any desired spot. It appears as a magic "cloth" in a related story, Tale CXX in the *Gesta Romanorum*, and it is a wishing cloak in "Donkey Cabbages," a variant in Grimms' *Household Tales* (No. 122). The narrator of our story seems to have forgotten the reason John wanted to visit the king's daughter. Doubtless he was attracted by the girl's beauty, for in the parallel episode in "Donkey Cabbages," the beauty of the daughter of a witch tempts the hero to enter her castle.

5. "The Wind Rider" is from *Folklore and Legend: Russian and Polish*, 1891, by C. J. T. A Polish tale. A witch turns the tables on an evil magician. Witches, of course, are famed for their power over the winds. According to an Italian tale, Judas's punishment was like this magician's. His soul was blown eternally around the world, and each day he passed the tamarind tree on which his body was hanging and saw it being torn by dogs and birds of prey.

6. "The Perspiring Lover" is the editor's shortened version of part of the Nala story in the *Mahabharata*. The chief point of interest in the tale is its depiction of the gods competing with a man for the hand of a mortal woman. Stanislao Prato has discovered a folk version of the Nala story in modern Tuscany.

7. "Strange Liaison" is from *Contes et Légendes Annamites*, 1886, by A. Landes. The editor's translation. The nameless beauty never gets to say a word.

8. "Sea Wife" is from *Fairy Legends and Traditions of the South of Ireland*, 1825-28, by Thomas Crofton Croker, where it is called "The Lady of

Gollerus." This fine story follows the traditional line of such tales, of which there are many.

9. "The Swan Princess" is from *Myths and Folklore of Ireland*, 1889, by Jeremiah Curtin, where it is called "The Three Daughters of the King of the East and the Son of a King of Erin." In the usual swan-maiden tale the swan becomes a wife because she cannot help it, her husband having stolen her swan skin, which she must have to resume her swan form. When she finds her feathers again, she flies away, leaving for good the man who had captured her.

10. "Thomas Rymer" is from *Demonology and Witchcraft*, 1830, by Sir Walter Scott. The great novelist's translation of the famous ballad about the fairy wife. He is not exactly explicit about what happened after Thomas "kissed her rosy lips underneath the Eildon tree," but it is easy to guess, for fairy women are notoriously wanton. The fairy queen's sudden loss of beauty has been explained in various ways: some think that for a moment her real nature is revealed—she is a spirit of the dead. The tradition of a teind or tithe which the fairies must pay from time to time to the Devil goes back to an old sacrifice made to the gods of the soil. Innumerable folktales warn against the danger of eating fairy food. The mortal who eats it can never return to his home again.

11. "Balkis, Queen of Sheba" is from *Legends of Old Testament Characters*, 1891, by S. Baring-Gould. The Mohammedan version. In both Moslem and Jewish tradition Solomon was not only a wise man but also a powerful magician. In our tale the mother of Balkis is the fairy wife with the usual taboo of not permitting questions about her origin. Asaph's powerful incantation with the ineffable name is a good example of name magic.

12. "The Girl Who Was Half-Married" is from the *Cent Nouvelles Nouvelles*, 1432-61 (No. 52), and is the editor's translation. We have here an interesting survival, the giving of the first night to a priest or a magician. Because he is protected by religion or magic, he braves the dangers of being the first to deflower a virgin. In Kamchatka as late as the eighteenth century a new husband was not permitted to sleep with a widow until somebody else had slept with her one night "to take away her sins." This somebody was usually a stranger, because dishonor was attached to the act. Doubtless in former times the stranger was nearly always a priest. In folktales it is very dangerous to be first or last.

13. "Nothing Like Stark Dead" is the Lady's Eighteenth Story in *The History of the Forty Vezirs*, 1886, translated by E. J. W. Gibb. A well-constructed and gripping Turkish tale, full of Oriental color.

14. "Women in Love" is from *Popular Tales from the Norse*, 1858, by Sir G. W. Dasent, where it is entitled "The Best Wish." The magic scissors, tablecloth and tap occur in about as many folktales as do seven-league boots, caps of invisibility and cudgels which work automatically.

15. "The Hasty Word" is from *Russian Folk-tales*, 1873, by W. R. S. Ralston. In folk belief a parent's "may the devil take you" is greatly to be feared. For example, in "The Seven Ravens" in Grimms' *Household Tales* (No. 25) a father's "hasty word" turns his six sons into ravens. In folktales the infernal regions are always easy of access, almost any well or cave leading down to it. Down there, as in fairyland, time runs much faster than in our world. Many versions of our tale were current in medieval Europe.

16. "The Bailie of London" is from *Popular Tales of the West Highlands*, 1860, by J. F. Campbell. The tale illustrates the folk belief in the reality of dreams.

17. "The King of Love" is from *Italian Popular Tales*, 1885, by T. F. Crane. Belongs to the Cupid-and-Psyche type. Notice the motif of the magically obstructed childbirth, which occurs also in the ballad of "Willie's Lady" and in Ovid's account of the birth of Hercules in the *Metamorphoses*.

18. "The Small-Tooth Dog" is from *Household Tales*, 1895, by S. O. Addy. Doubtless this tale also belongs to, or is closely related to, the Cupid-and-Psyche type. When the little wife says the right words in the right place the spell that has been cast on her mate is broken.

19. "The Horse-Devil and the Witch" is from *Turkish Fairy Tales and Folk Tales*, 1896, by Ignatius Kunos, and is the translation of R. Nisbet Bain. A splendid version of the Cupid-and-Psyche story. The witch is asked to swear "by the egg," the egg being a symbol of the soul and sovereign against the evil eye because it has no opening and is, so to speak, impregnable.

20. "The Dead Lover" is from the *Ocean of the Streams of Story*, 1884, translated by C. H. Tawney. Here, as often in folktales, the dead are depicted as being in a torpid state or lethargic sleep, and awakening from time to time and feeling hunger. It is a custom in many countries to place food in or beside the tombs of the deceased, and in some places to let down provisions by a pipe into the grave. Sometimes food is actually applied to the mouth of a dead person.

21. "The Sneezing Bride" is from *Fairy Legends and Traditions of the South of Ireland*, 1825-28, by Thomas Crofton Croker. The leprechaun, shoemaker and guardian of fairy treasure, and the cluricaune or lurikeen, his equivalent in southwest Ireland, are solitary fairies. Often the cluricaune haunts wine cellars and frightens the wits out of servants who go to fetch wine. From

remotest antiquity sneezing has been regarded as ominous. The basis of the superstition is the notion that the soul is easily dislodged and therefore the sneezer is in danger of losing his. It is customary to wish well to the sneezer and invoke blessings upon him. Long before the "God bless you" or "*Gesundheit*" came "May Jupiter preserve you," and the like.

A witch in W. Webster's *Basque Legends*, 1877 (No 73), was able to slay all the children of a certain family. When a child sneezed and nobody took the trouble to say, "*Domine stekan*" (corruption of *Domine tecum*), she took its soul. A child's soul is considered especially weak.

22. "Donagha Dee and His Wife" is from *Killarney Legends*, 1853, by Thomas Crofton Croker, where it is entitled "The Legend of Tig-na-Vauria."

23. "The Specter Bridegroom" is from *Popular Romances of the West of England*, 1871, by Robert Hunt. Slightly shortened. A Low German tale somewhat similar to this story was the basis of Bürger's famous "Lenore," which was written in 1773.

The sowing of the hemp on Allhallows Eve is by no means confined to Scotland. After the hemp is sown, the ground is usually harrowed by anything the girl can drag after her. Then the rhyme as given here is repeated and the girl, looking over her left shoulder, will see the appearance of her lover in the attitude of pulling hemp. Iron, so dreaded by otherworld creatures, counteracts all magic. The blacksmith's iron was powerful enough to break the grip of Frank's ghost on Nancy.

24. "In the Magic Mountains" is from *Georgian Folk Tales*, 1894, by Marjory Wardrop, where it is entitled "The Story of Dervish." These magic mountains are like the Thessaly of Apuleius, where the incantations of magic are indigenous, and magic springs, shape-shifting and swans that cause nightmares belong to the usual train of events. Perhaps there is an echo or two from *The Golden Ass* in our story.

25. "The Frog's Skin" is also from *Georgian Folk Tales*, 1894, by Marjory Wardrop. An interesting variant of the Cupid-and-Psyche type as the usual roles are reversed, the heroine being the one who is in animal form. Note that the burning of the skin takes away the power of transformation. The couples on the axhandle and the bullock's skin illustrate the text in the Talmud which runs, "While our love was strong, we lay on the edge of a sword; now a couch sixty yards wide is too narrow for us."

26. "The Man with the Evil Eye" is from *Folklore and Legend; Russian and Polish*, 1891, by C. J. T. This dramatic tale is of Polish origin. An account in the *Gentleman's Magazine Library*, III, 287-91, describes a certain Christian Malford as being an involuntary *gettatore*, like the chief character

in our story. Malford's malignant glances caused the death of his own farm animals, and he was reduced to great poverty.

When witches possess the evil eye, which is nearly always, they employ it intentionally as one of their deadliest weapons. There are hundreds of ways to protect oneself against the evil eye still used every day nearly everywhere. The Zadik, a rabbi well-versed in cabalistic doctrine, gives a talisman, a round bit of parchment on which are written unintelligible phrases of Chaldean Hebrew, to the mother who fears that her child has been overlooked, that is, harmed by the *aïn-ra* or *ainhoré*. The sign of the fig or horn is the most famous of these countercharms. Horns, ribbons arranged in the shape of a horn, horseshoes with points turned upward, phallic symbols, a wolf's tooth, spitting on the right shoe, a dirty face, an uneven haircut, wearing clothes inside out, wearing a veil or a disguise, and numberless other countercharms are still in constant use somewhere in the world.

27. "The Cat-Woman" is from *Folklore de l'Ille-et-Vilaine*, 1898, by Adolph Orain. The editor's translation. A variant of the werewolf theme. In some versions the woman leaves her skin under the bed, transforms herself into an animal and goes out to *courir le gilledou*, as the French folk say. In some West Indian and Negro versions the woman's husband gets revenge on her by sprinkling salt and pepper into the skin she leaves behind, and, when she puts it on at her return, it burns her badly and frequently kills her.

28. "The White Mouse" is from *Hessische Sagen*, 1853, by J. W. Wolf. The editor's translation. In folktales the soul is often represented as a mouse which leaves the sleeping person and wanders forth. It must return to the sleeper before he can wake up. In the story the maiden "dies" because her soul-mouse has been captured and cannot return. She revives the moment it comes back to her. Nightmares are often thought to be the souls of sleeping women.

29. "The Clever Knight" is from the *Gesta Romanorum*, Tale CXXIV. The editor's version of this smart little fabliau.

30. "Hackelnberg and the Screech Owl" is from *Local Popular Traditions of the Harz Mountains*, by J. C. C. Nachtigal, in *German Novelists*, 1826, by Thomas Roscoe. A fine tale belonging to the Wild Hunt type. On his deathbed Hackelnberg, passionately fond of the chase, would not listen to the priest or hearken to his mention of heaven. "I care not for heaven," he muttered. "I care only for the hunt." "Then hunt until the Last Day," cried the priest. So through the chilly blast, the rain and the snow Hackelnberg with his hounds leads the Wild Hunt or Furious Host on an eternal hunt.

The tradition of the Wild Hunt is known to have existed in ancient Greece and in India. The leader, often a noted malefactor, is the Devil, or

Hackelnberg, or King Herla, or Herne the Hunter, or the Irish magician O'Donoghue. In Scandinavia he is Odin, in England he may be King Arthur; in Germany it may be Frau Berchta or Holde, and she is usually attended by troups of unbaptized children, often in the forms of dogs. In certain parts of France the leader is Herod, and he is on the hunt for Jewish children. In Catalonia the Wild Hunt is said to be Herodias dancing the eternal dance she was condemned to perform for bringing about the death of John the Baptist.

The story of the Wandering Jew and the tale of the Flying Dutchman are related to the Wild Hunt type.

31. "The Devil in Skirts" is from *Niederländische Sagen,* 1843, by J. W. Wolf. The editor's translation. A fine devil story with an undertone of old romance. The old hermit is like the sage Apollonius in Keats's *Lamia.*

32. "Lady Good Luck" is from *Old Deccan Days,* 1881, by Mary Frere, where it is called "Sodewa Bai." A tale of the separable soul. Sodewa Bai's half-death illustrates the primitive idea of death as a kind of sleep from which there are occasional awakenings.

33. "Samson and His Woman" is from *The History of the Forty Vezirs,* 1886, the translation of E. J. W. Gibb. An interesting version of the most famous of all tales of the separable soul. Here the original idea of the giant's hiding his soul (strength, heart) in some secret place as a protective measure is lost, and the strength is transferred from Samson's hair to that of his paramour. Now witches have the power of strengthening their hair, a few strands of it, until it can hold off mighty beasts, such as bears and lions, that would harm them. This witch tradition dominates this part of the story. It is to be noted that Samson is never mentioned in the Koran.

34. "The Stealing of the Heart" is from the *Ocean of the Streams of Story,* 1884, the translation of C. H. Tawney. The maiden steals the heart (soul, strength) of her dead lover and returns him to life. The dismay of the keeper of the elephants at the birth in the stable was chiefly caused by fear of the blood. The wonderful stone referred to is a talisman, a palladium upon which the safety of the kingdom depends.

35. "La Donna Mobile" is from *The History of the Forty Vezirs,* 1886, translated by E. J. W. Gibb. A Turkish fabliau.

36. "Hacon Grizzlebeard" is from *Popular Tales from the Norse,* 1858, by G. W. Dasent. A popular *Taming of the Shrew.* Well-known versions of it are: "King Thrushbeard" in Grimms' *Household Tales,* No. 52; "The Crumb in the Beard" in T. F. Crane's *Italian Popular Tales;* and "Pride Punished" in Basile's *Pentameron,* IV:10.

37. "Beauty Treatment" is from *Sicilianische Märchen*, 1870, by Laura Gonzenbach, the translation of T. F. Crane in *Italian Popular Tales*, 1885. A satire on the vanity of women which age cannot destroy. A well-known variant is "The Old Woman Discovered" in Basile's *Pentameron*, I:10.

38. "The Devil Tries Marriage" is from *The Facetious Nights* of Straparola, II:4. The editor's shortened version. A fabliau. The trick played to get the Devil to leave the body of the person he is tormenting occurs in many tales about bad wives. For example, it is in "The Bad Wife" in *Russian Folktales*, 1873, by W. R. S. Ralston. The demon is an *ifrit* in a Turkish variant in *The History of the Forty Vezirs*, 1886 (the 27th Vezir's Story). The gift of a demon or fairy often changes into ashes or something as worthless.

39. "The Laird of Balmachie's Wife" is from *Folklore and Legends: Scotland*, 1892, by C. J. T. When fairies steal a wife they leave a log of wood, hollowed out beneath, or one of their own people as a substitute. In our story the steel sword and the calling upon the Deity are strong countercharms and deprive the fairies of their power.

40. "The O'Donoghue in the Lake" is from *Folklore and Legends: Ireland*, 1892, by C. J. T. O'Donoghue is the most famous of Irish wizards and appears in many folktales.